THE BACK HOME SERIES

Series Titles

The Arc of the Escarpment
Robert Root

Soul of the Outdoors
Dave Greschner

We Come from Good Stock
Kay Oakes Oring

Squatter
Yolanda DeLoach

Wildlifer
Neil F. Payne

From the Heart: The Story of Matrix
John Harmon

The Long Fields
Anne-Marie Oomen

Kick Out the Bottom
Erik Mortenson & Christopher Kramer

Wrong Tree: Adventures in Wildlife Biology
Jeff Wilson

At the Lake
Jim Landwehr

Body Talk
Takwa Gordon

The In-Between State
Martha Lundin

North Freedom
Carolyn Dallmann

Ohio Apertures
Robert Miltner

Praise for

The Arc of the Escarpment

"Moving through landscapes of erosion and uplift, collapse and contortion, Root might be looking for what defines him and his home, but he offers us even more: the reminder that when we know more about not just who and where we are but also when we are, we can begin to wrestle with the fallacy of arbitrary boundaries and to understand—deeply—the value of humility. What a satisfyingly provocative read."

—Barbara Hurd
author of *The Epilogues*

"'Always alert for synchronicity,' Robert Root takes us along his nature hikes as he follows the Niagara Escarpment. His exacting descriptions illuminate his observations: natural springs, sink holes, caves with spots of hungry mud, gorges, creeks, ravines, alvars and grikes (the latter big enough to shelter bears), dancing sand, lighthouses, grottos, arches, waterfalls, and plunge pools. And he enriches these stories of stone and scalloped shorelines with research, revealing a stunning breadth of history held in shapes that glaciers made."

—Christine Stewart-Nuñez
author of *Chrysopoeia: Essays of Language, Love, and Place*

"In the tradition of Loren Eiseley and Robin Wall Kimmerer, Bob Root offers the reader a chance to take his hand and go on a journey under the skin of complex ecologies. Over a lifetime of observation and contemplation of human and more than human ecologists in the fulsome Great Lakes region, this writer brings to bear a wealth of detail and insights that traverse time and ecological thought. As we huddle and contend with climate change, Root is with us as he records and reveres specific, complex places and indigenous knowledge of place, so essential to understanding what it means to be human now."

—Leslie Carol Roberts
author of *The Entire Earth and Sky: Views on Antarctica*

THE ARC OF THE ESCARPMENT

The Arc of the Escarpment

a narrative of place

Robert Root

CORNERSTONE PRESS
UNIVERSITY OF WISCONSIN-STEVENS POINT

Cornerstone Press, Stevens Point, Wisconsin 54481
Copyright © 2024 Robert Root
www.uwsp.edu/cornerstone

Printed in the United States of America by
Point Print and Design Studio, Stevens Point, Wisconsin

Library of Congress Control Number: 2023950465
ISBN: 978-1-960329-25-7

Photographs by Robert Root.

This is a work of nonfiction. All of the events in this book are true to the best of the author's memory. Some names and identifying features have been changed to protect the identity of certain parties. The author in no way represents any company, corporation, or brand, mentioned herein. The views expressed in this memoir are solely those of the author.

Cornerstone Press titles are produced in courses and internships offered by the Department of English at the University of Wisconsin–Stevens Point.

DIRECTOR & PUBLISHER   EXECUTIVE EDITORS
Dr. Ross K. Tangedal   Jeff Snowbarger, Freesia McKee

EDITORIAL DIRECTOR   SENIOR EDITORS
Ellie Atkinson   Brett Hill, Grace Dahl

PRESS STAFF
Chloe Ciezynski, Carolyn Czerwinski, Alex Diaz, Kirsten Faulkner, Sophie McPherson, Kylie Newton, Eva Nielsen, Josh Paulson, Natalie Reiter, Lauren Rudesill, Katie Schimke, Anthony Thiel, Cam Williams, Ava Willett

*To those who shared my time
whenever and wherever I've been
within the arc of the Escarpment*

Also by Robert Root:

Lineage: Reading the Past to Reach the Present

Walking Home Ground: In the Footsteps of Muir, Leopold, and Derleth

Happenstance

Limited Sight Distance: Essays for Airwaves

Postscripts: Retrospections on Time and Place

Following Isabella: Travels in Colorado Then and Now

The Nonfictionist's Guide: On Reading and Writing Creative Nonfiction

Landscapes With Figures: The Nonfiction of Place

Recovering Ruth: A Biographer's Tale

The Fourth Genre: Contemporary Writers of/on Creative Nonfiction

E. B. White: The Emergence of an Essayist

— Contents —

List of Photographs

Wisconsin

Boundary Waters, Part One

Michigan

Boundary Waters, Part Two

Ontario

The Gorge

New York

"Place and a mind may interpenetrate till the nature of both is altered. I cannot tell what this movement is except by recounting it."

—Nan Shepherd, *The Living Mountain*

Prologue

Thinking about geology requires an energetic imagination. Standing at a road cut anywhere it bisected a hill, you gaze at ten to thirty feet of exposed earth marveling that a path so wide was carved through such a mass. Imagining how that earthen mass came to be there takes more effort. In books like John McPhee's *Annals of the Former World*, we learn geologists appreciate examining the earth being opened up this way. As you pass through, you consider the height, but if you climb over such a hill prior to roadwork, you have little sense of what you stand on, except for what you scoop up at your feet. These manmade cliff faces and bluffs—essentially unnatural scarps—expose the natural history of particular patches of ground.

Standing on the roadside you might ponder how long it took to deposit all that earth from the level under your feet to the top of the cut, what natural process performed it, how long it'd been accumulating and how much deeper below you'd find bedrock, where deposition began, the foundational floor of the earth supporting you. If you're standing near the Great Lakes, where massive glacial Ice Age incursions scraped away layer after layer of that deposition, you might feel overwhelmed by the scale of what you're trying to understand.

Or at least I might. And do.

I earned an average grade in college Earth Science. No matter how often I review divisions in the Geologic Time Scale—*eons* divided into *eras* divided into *periods* divided into *epochs* divided into *ages*—I need a visual aid to recall where a specific eon, era, period, or epoch fits when it shows up in my reading. Precambrian, happily, starts with "pre," and the Precambrian Eon came before the Cambrian Period, the earliest period in the Paleozoic Era of the Phanerozoic Eon that succeeded the Precambrian (Shouldn't be it called the Prephanerozoic, since they're both eons?). Already, you can tell, I'm in trouble. The Precambrian Eon dates from between 4600 million and 542 million years ago and the Phanerozoic from 542 MYA (as geologists abbreviate it) until now. The Phanerozoic divides into three eras: the Paleozoic Era, (542–251 MYA); the Mesozoic (251–c. 65 MYA), the dinosaur era; and the Cenozoic (65 MYA to the present), with three periods, the most recent—the Quaternary—beginning around 2,588 MYA and consisting of two epochs, the Pleistocene (ending 11,000 years ago) and the Holocene. We live in the Phanerozoic Eon, the Cenozoic Era, the Quaternary Period, and the Holocene Epoch, the most recent divisions of each unit of time, though some argue for the present as the Anthropocene, the human epoch.

Materials forming the Niagara Escarpment were deposited in the Silurian Period, the third Paleozoic period, dating from 443.7 to 416.7 million years ago. What we presently see around the Great Lakes resulted from roughly the past 17,000 years of earth history; it's on top of what resulted from 400,000,000 years of earth history. That I can walk around on and touch material formed in the Silurian Period means that everything that might have been deposited between the Silurian and the Holocene—during eight geologic periods and one geologic epoch, roughly 399,989,000 years of possible deposits—is missing in those locations, because, in all that time, erosion rather than deposition was the primary geologic force at play. This gives me a sense of scale about the geological history I hope to understand.

Plate tectonics models show Earth's landmasses moving all over the globe, breaking apart and colliding and reforming and shifting climates. In the Silurian Period, North America's present center was near the equator, more tropical or subtropical in climate. Because of higher sea levels and extensive melting of polar ice caps (a situation now recurring), the central continent was under a shallow sea. As in any ocean, deposition built up. Silurian deposits of plant and animal life differed in character from those of Ordovician and Cambrian deposits below them and Devonian, Carboniferous, and Permian deposits that rose above them. Evidence of the Silurian Period is buried deeply under deposits of all those succeeding periods, except notably around the Great Lakes.

Over immense amounts of time the North American plate slid away from the equator, the climate changed, sea levels dropped, and shallow seas receded. In the Pleistocene Epoch, about a million years ago, a period of global cooling initiated a sequence of glaciation that essentially involved four major occurrences, all moving south from the Canadian or Laurentian Shield. At their farthest, the glaciers reached deep into what is now northeast Kansas, middle Missouri, and southern Illinois, Indiana, and Ohio, and covered all of New York and New England; the final ice sheet, known as the Wisconsin Glaciation, did not extend quite so far. Together these glaciers, in their advances and recessions, determined the nature of the landscape they crossed, developing the Great Lakes and the valleys of the St. Lawrence, Mississippi, Missouri, and Ohio Rivers. In the Great Lakes region, they scoured depositions of millennia off the surface and their melting further eroded the terrain and added depositions of till and outwash. They also depressed the land to form an immense basin that the Great Lakes partially filled with meltwater once the glaciers receded. Having worked their way across soft sedimentary depositions, glaciers exposed, bumped up against, and climbed over harder Silurian dolostone deposits that make up what we call the Niagara Escarpment. When the glaciers receded and their meltwaters were more stable through the formation of lakes and rivers, the Niagara Escarpment remained exposed and, often, prominent.

If you follow exposed sections of the Niagara Escarpment from where it appears above ground in central New York State, west across the Niagara River into Ontario, northwest up the Bruce Peninsula to arch across Michigan's Upper Peninsula and veer southwest down the Door Peninsula into Wisconsin, until it disappears underground again—or reverse that trajectory—the Escarpment forms a shepherd's crook, Bo-Peep's question-mark-shaped staff, pictured that way on many maps. But that shape only highlights the most prominent outcroppings and doesn't account for underground extensions. Whenever I gaze at tourist features like Niagara Falls or Flowerpot Island or the Door Peninsula, I remember that the Niagara formation is more than its surface show. If we brought the glaciers back to dig a little deeper along the southern reaches of the Great Lakes, the loop we'd expose would turn the shepherd's crook into a tennis racket or a frying pan; scrape more broadly and the Michigan Basin would become a large dent in a relatively flat griddle. Raise that dent so the Silurian depositions form one continuous surface, and you find them spread over a vast area of central North America. Niagara dolostone is sometimes exposed near the southern shore of Lake Erie, though connection to Niagara Falls or to Wisconsin outcroppings seems impossibly remote.

The Niagara Escarpment tends to be an encompassing term, but it is insufficiently descriptive. An escarpment is a cliff-face, an abrupt perpendicular surface; behind the edge of the escarpment is a considerable landmass called a cuesta, a gently sloping ridge that can form a significant plain. The scarp is the exposed portion of the cuesta that has eroded away and, over time, continues to erode away, reducing the size of the cuesta. We think of an escarpment in terms of the view up its face from its base but when we move across the top of the escarpment we move across the cuesta.

All along the Niagara Escarpment people are aware of its unique properties and features—life forms that thrive only on the scarp face, the kind of microclimate it generates, the fossils found within its rocks, even what wines grow best in the cuesta's soil. It is the subject of both intense scrutiny and lively celebration, of investigations into its geology, botany, zoology, paleontology, anthropology, hydrology, and meteorology, of expanding efforts at preservation, restoration, recreation, education and tourism. When we look closely, we realize there's a lot to learn along the arc of the Escarpment.

Born and raised near one end of the shepherd's crook, I spent a good portion of my adult life within its arc and now, late in life, live on the other end. I sometimes feel the escarpment inviting me to get to know it more fully than I have over all those decades, even if it means doing my Earth Science class again entirely on my own. And so, I follow the arc of the Escarpment from where I will likely end back to where I began. I'll travel across space and to some degree across time to learn what I can about what has underlain the landscape of most of my life, the arc of the Escarpment.

Wisconsin

Four hundred million years ago, shallow, clear, warm Silurian seas were, like tropical seas today, hospitable to coral, which built immense reefs that compacted into dolostone, the highly resistant rock of the Niagara Escarpment. Glacial masses from Canada removed softer, later deposits, exposed Silurian rocks, and replaced millions of years of soil with glacial debris. Three quarters of Wisconsin's surface are glacial in origin, and some Silurian outliers remain in the Driftless area—the Niagara dolostone caps of Blue Mound and nearby Platte, Belmont, and Sinsinawa Mounds. Erosion removed the strata surrounding them, just as the Escarpment's cliff face appears after soft lower rock layers weather away until unsupported capstone collapses into a talus heap.

The Niagara Escarpment underlies the easternmost edge of Wisconsin, on the western border of the Michigan Basin. Its cuesta slopes toward Lake Michigan; the scarp faces Green Bay along the Door Peninsula and interior Wisconsin for the remainder of its length. The slope averages about 12 feet per mile, from around an elevation of 1,000 feet in Waukesha County to around 700 feet near the lake shoreline. Glacial deposits in southern counties add to the elevation. The cuesta's width varies from 7-20 miles at its northern end on the Door Peninsula to 25-45 miles wide at its southern end near the Illinois border. It forms the upland between Lake Michigan and the Green Bay, Lake Winnebago, and the Rock River lowlands. To drive from Lake Michigan inland to anywhere you might see the Niagara Escarpment, you ride above and sometimes on the Niagara Cuesta. Niagaran limestone/dolostone strata can be between 450 to 800 feet thick, and the height of exposed sections of escarpment runs from 160 to 220 feet in northern reaches, from 200 to 300 feet in central reaches.

During the Wisconsin Glaciation, the Niagara Escarpment deflected the Laurentide Ice Sheet sufficiently to form two distinct lobes. The Lake Michigan Lobe covered the area surrounding Lake Michigan and extended as far south as Illinois and Indiana; the Green Bay Lobe flowed over Wisconsin almost to the Illinois border and across the east central portion of the state. In that glacial episode other lobes further west came only a third of the way down the state. Drumlins, eskers, kames, moraines, and kettles left behind by an ice sheet estimated to be thousands of feet thick are everywhere across the present landscape; till, outwash, and glacial erratics give continuous testimony to the way that landscape was formed.

In eastern Wisconsin, glacial deposits formed the ridges and lowlands of the Kettle Moraine, which sprawls across the interlobate area between the Green Bay and Lake Michigan Lobes for 120 miles between Walworth County in the south and Sheboygan County in the north; some geologists argue it continues further north with less prominence and official recognition. In Washington and Waukesha counties the Niagara Escarpment runs under and sometimes alongside the Kettle Moraine and is visible east of Horicon Marsh, Lake Winnebago, and the Fox River. From the city of Green Bay north, it overlooks Green Bay from its eastern shoreline and underlies Washington Island and Rock Island, the last Wisconsin bodies of land before the open passage between the Door Peninsula and islands marking the border of Michigan's Upper Peninsula. From Brady's Rocks in Waukesha County to Rock Island, the Niagara Escarpment extends roughly 250 miles, sometimes hidden underground, often the most prominent part of the landscape, always a vital part of the terrain.

Scientist and naturalist Increase Allen Lapham recognized the arc of the Escarpment early on. As a young man, he worked on carving the Erie Canal through the Escarpment at Lockport in western New York. He explained the arc in an 1851 letter to his wife: "This remarkable limestone ledge forms the Niagara Falls, then sweeping through Canada and upper Michigan, turns to the south along the east side of Green Bay and Lake Winnebago and is lost only at Ashippun in Dodge County, Wisconsin." Ashippun and Dodge County are northwest of Brady's Rocks in Waukesha County, which Lapham never saw. The possibility of separate terminal sites suggests that the Escarpment isn't one continuous geological formation but a series of outcroppings and exposures of Niagaran dolostone formed in the Silurian period. Erosion can separate segments of the Escarpment and create distinctive outliers. In southeastern Wisconsin connection between outcroppings at Ashippun and Brady's Rocks still exist, buried under glacial debris, just as an island chain indicates a connected landmass beneath an ocean.

For me, Brady's Rocks is the above ground western terminus of the Niagara Escarpment. It's in the county where I live, 25 miles away from where we moved to be close to one of our daughters and her family. Always alert for synchronicity, I felt the nearness of an Escarpment outcropping made settling here especially appropriate, then gradually felt the need to trace the Escarpment back to where I began, in that Escarpment town of Lockport. I start that journey from where I am, where I am likely to be in time to come. I start at Brady's Rocks.

1

Silurian dolomite underlays much of Waukesha County, where industry has often exposed it to view. *The History of Waukesha County* (1880) claimed the "cheapness with which buildings have always been erected in Waukesha County" was due to "the abundance and excellence of the stone which is quarried at almost every desirable point." The stone in the Prairieville Academy, the county's oldest stone structure and the state's first stone-built educational building, came from a quarry opened in 1840. The building subsequently was the site, from 1846 to 1848, of Carroll College, the first college chartered in Wisconsin Territory; later, as the First German Reformed Church, it was torn down in 1891. The relocated Carroll College's first Main Hall was erected in 1852 and replaced in 1885, both times in Waukesha stone.

The *History* described Waukesha stone as "a close-textured, light-colored magnesian stone, of which many of the business blocks and private residences of the county seat are constructed," including the Fountain Spring House, a 500-room hotel prominent in Waukesha's late nineteenth-century resort era; St. Joseph's Catholic Church; and the Waukesha County Courthouse. Readers were assured of the stone's "almost infinite" durability and "practically inexhaustible" supply. Thirteen thriving stone quarries in the county, most with established lime kilns, produced "almost pure oxide of calcium. . . . the whitest and strongest lime in the market."

Niagara dolomite is easily confused with limestone and the term limestone was generally applied to dolomite or dolostone formations. Limestone and dolomite are both sedimentary rocks formed by the deposition of living matter—corals, clams, snails and the like—over an immense period of time in shallow seas. Limestone contains more than 50 percent calcite (calcium carbonate) and dolomite (calcium magnesium carbonate), but if dolomite comes to be more abundant than calcite, the formation is considered dolostone, a harder substance than limestone.

In Waukesha, though Prairieville Academy and the Fountain House are long gone, other landmark stone buildings abound. Some of the original Waukesha Public Library's stone exterior, dedicated in 1901 and since remodeled and expanded, is still visible. The impressive St. Joseph's Catholic Church abuts the sidewalk. The imposing Waukesha County Historical Museum, formerly the Waukesha County Courthouse, rises three-and-a-half stories to a steep roof with gabled dormers, rounded turrets on each corner; on the north side a square tower topped by a domed cupola rises another three stories. As a courthouse it projected great gravity; as a historical museum it aptly reminds us of the past; as a massive building composed of Waukesha stone it is the most impressive artifact in Waukesha County.

I intend to concentrate on the Escarpment and its cuesta as themselves, but when I enter the Public Library or the Historical Museum or pass the Catholic Church, I'm aware that, even if people feel no connection to the stone, it's not only an element of the remote past but an essential element of the lives they live now.

* * *

Waukesha County histories emphasize "Waukesha stone," but elsewhere the term most often used is "Lannon stone." A multitude of houses in our daughter's Milwaukee neighborhood have Lannon stone facades. A series of small quarries, white spaces contrasting starkly with the green of farms and parks and neighborhoods in an aerial view, veer northeast from Waukesha through Lannon, including one site where two broad white strips alternate with two wide blue ponds, where Lannon stone comes from.

The Niagaran Age of the middle Silurian Period, when the dolostone strata estimated to be as much as 600 feet thick was created, lasted around twelve million years; for a century and a half, quarries have attempted to remove as much of those strata as possible. To appreciate the scale of the Silurian depositions, to sense the depth and dimension to these quarries, requires an on-the-ground perspective

The closest quarries are just north of town, on either side of a four-lane highway, the eastern one virtually inaccessible, even from Niagara Street, Niagara Court, and Falls Court, the western one more open to view despite the frantic pace of traffic. I make a risky turn into a large, paved area for Waukesha Lime and Stone, immediately aware it isn't an actual parking lot. Luckily, no heavy machinery moves around me. I park between two steep entrances into the quarry, then walk a short way to an overlook area above the quarry floor.

The view provides a sense of scale. The quarry, deep and wide, extends two-thirds of a mile along the road. Trees growing at the base of its walls get no higher than a third of the way up and trees on top of them are no more than a third as tall. The walls are sheer cliff faces, quarried for decades, and their upper reaches likely haven't been scraped for stone in a long time. The sparse plant growth on the cliff face testifies to its being a mechanical creation rather than a natural one. What makes Silurian dolostone so popular is its tendency not only to be the hardest stone but also to break off in blocks and layers. Here the top fifty feet or so of layers are the same color and form a distinctly different wall section than the darker, less uniform layers below. Dolomitic limestone ranges from the top of the wall to the bottom of the quarry.

Lannon, eleven miles northeast of Waukesha, near Menomonee Falls, began quarrying Niagara dolostone in 1838, shortly after the village was settled. More than thirty quarries operated in the area. I pass several quarrying and stonework sites on my drive to Menomonee Park, a county park sprawling across 470 acres with a 16-acre lake at the center. Quarry Lake is simply the water-filled remains of a Lannon quarry, with a sandy beach on one side, a scuba diving area on another, and stone crusher remains overlooking the lake. Layers of stone rise a few feet above the surface and the beach house and fence posts are constructed of quarried stone. With the lake so broad, the waters so calm, the shoreline lined with trees, it would be easy to think the site was a natural formation rather than an industrial one.

East of Lannon, turning north onto a wishbone-shaped gravel road, I immediately see into one of the two quarries there. I park and walk to the line of stones marking the shoulder, a steep drop just beyond them and a large, almost square body of water below, its depth hard to gauge. The stark cliff face of the northern wall, a sheer white vertical precipice, is similar to the eastern wall I stand on. A low, flat, white stone shelf extends down the pool's west side, then turns to run along the south wall. High mounds of gravel and crushed stone perch on the shelf, on either side of long, raised conveyer tracks. The shelf walls are lower than other walls but just as sheer. The flat horizontal and vertical surfaces make it easy to see how the layers of stone have been removed.

I drive to the tip of the wishbone and turn south between the quarries. Massive chunks of rock or wire fence or both line each side of the road. The western quarry seems a little less deep, with more open surfaces and more stacks of stone piled neatly and systematically. From a waist-high rectangle of dolostone, I look at a second pond in the eastern quarry, separated from the other by that shelf running down the center, and a road descending along the north wall ends on it. Where the shelf meets the south wall, I spot a cave cut back into the stone.

I can't tell if stonecutters have plumbed the limits of Niagaran strata, but judge the ponds to be very deep, those sheer walls going a long way underwater to reach the final depths. Here again I sense what the Silurian period deposited and what lies beneath the surface everywhere I hope to see outcroppings of the Niagara Escarpment in Wisconsin. I remember waves lapping the Lake Michigan shore, shifting sand in their ebb and flow, and try to imagine how long such action in Silurian seas went on to build such walls as these I see here. The principle of sedimentation is easy to understand but the results of it on a scale like this are hard to imagine happening.

* * *

The Niagara Escarpment put me in touch with the Ice Age Trail. I could only reach Brady's Rocks on the Ice Age Trail. My wife and I later hiked with IAT members through woods on a slope of the Escarpment on the outskirts of Hartland. Walking all 45 miles of the Trail in Waukesha County, we often hiked terrain rising above the Escarpment, though only Brady's Rocks preserved a prominent outcropping.

The Ice Age Trail follows the edge of the Green Bay Lobe through eastern and central parts of the state and the edges of other, shorter lobes west to the Minnesota border. More than 600 of a proposed 1,200-mile-long trail are complete, running east from Interstate Park on the St. Croix River two-thirds of the way across the state, meandering south to counties on the border with Illinois, looping around to extend at a northeast angle to the coast of Lake Michigan, and ending in Potawatomi Park on the Door Peninsula. Niagaran strata lies somewhere under most of the eastern wing of the trail, but only in Waukesha County is the Niagara Escarpment a palpable presence on the trail. In the Kettle Moraine State Forest, encompassing much of a discontinuous 120-mile stretch of terrain, the Escarpment underlies the two southernmost units, Lapham Peak and Southern Kettle Moraine, and spills out, like the Kettle Moraine itself, beyond the borders of the State Forest.

Glacial deposits obscure the presence of the Escarpment below much of the Ice Age Trail in Waukesha County, including the prominent and popular segment at Lapham Peak. At 1,233 feet above sea level, it's the highest point in Waukesha County, a 45-foot tower perched at its "peak." It is actually a glacial hill, named for Increase Lapham, who in 1870 initiated the idea of a national weather service by forecasting conditions from here. Recurring periods of erosion and glaciation scoured evidence of subsequent geologic periods off the surface of Niagaran strata, but here that layer has largely been covered up by glacial depositions of considerable mass.

From Lapham Peak State Park south, the Ice Age Trail eventually traces the western side of the Kettle Moraine through the Waterville segment. According to *The Geology of the Ice Age Scenic Trail*, here the trail rises to "the edge of the Niagara Escarpment" and then "follows near the crest of the more than 100-foot-high, steep slope." The trail leads through lowlands, then under tall trees and through thick forest undergrowth, and soon crosses rolling terrain with steep slopes. I walked it gawking at old, large oaks and sandhill cranes stalking through an open hayfield, and soon noticed outcroppings of buried dolomite in the center of the trail and distinctive rocks to the side. For a little while, I clearly walked a lightly exposed section of the Escarpment.

Brady's Rocks are further south, in the IAT's Eagle segment. I hike, admiring century-old oaks and places where leaf fall keeps the forest floor open. In the Kettle Moraine Low Prairie Natural Area, rolling flatlands where in fall the grasses are higher than my head, I spot two bluebirds, a yellow warbler, a common yellowthroat, and a bobolink, welcome signs of spring. Atop a grassy knoll a Leopold bench invites a moment of gazing off across the low prairie, where efforts at restoration through controlled burns and tree removal have made the Scuppernong River Habitat Area the largest wet prairie east of the Mississippi.

Here the landscape begins to resemble its pre-settlement status. The lowlands west of the Trail are in the former bed of Glacial Lake Scuppernong, a vast area of impounded meltwater that spread across the whole of what is now neighboring Jefferson County and the edges of five other counties. Here, the 2,013 acres of the Scuppernong River Habitat Area contains the Scuppernong Prairie Natural Area (180 acres), a restored wet-mesic prairie, and Kettle Moraine Low Prairie State Natural Area (250 acres), comprising both wet-mesic and dry-mesic prairie. Walking through the natural areas and scanning the lowlands, it's possible to imagine what the landscape looked like before settlement by European-Americans in the early nineteenth century. When the wind drowns out the distant traffic sounds and you stand near a cluster of bur oaks overlooking swaying grasses filling the space to your horizon, you can conjure the sense of being in a different time. You can imagine Michael and Kathleen Brady seeing it for the first time in the middle of the nineteenth century.

The trail descends to a mid-slope section leading to the Brady's Rocks loop, once off on a side trail but in recent years rerouted by the Waukesha-Milwaukee Chapter of the Ice Age Trail Alliance to give easier access to the rocks. The Bradys were Irish immigrants. Remnants of a stone rubble fence are largely all that remains of the farm they established here in 1855. Brady quarried some of the stone in this section and outcroppings perching on the side of the slope are the most exposed evidence of the Niagara Escarpment in the county. If you're looking for a place to witness the end (or the beginning) of the arc of the Escarpment, this is the place to come.

In the loop, I pass between rock formations often shoulder-height, head-height, and higher, surrounded by dense vegetation. Random blocks of stone are visible on the ground, often completely coated in thick coverings of moss. In one place a fallen tree lays between two small turrets, their layers mirroring one another, parts of one continuous whole separated by millennia of erosion. All around me are layers of different colored rocks, capstone layers bumpy, weathered, and uneven, lower layers more even but marked by crevices, ledges, and shelves. Here on a small scale is evidence of how resistant the top layers are and how the layers below them are more easily erodible, undercutting support for the surface layers. At the top of the slope the stone is more uniform and secure, its cuesta flat and hard to see. The loop takes me past large freestanding blocks and short stone towers, all separate from one another. Signs of a continuous wall of exposed stone are evident in some places, though plant life in a wet season sometimes curtains off sections. The area is well-shaded. Distinctive ferns include cliff brake, fragile fern, and the intriguing walking fern, which can grow a new fern when a leaf tip touches wet ground and thus "walk" across its habitat. The cracks and crevices formed by erosion in the dolomite make it hospitable to resilient plant life.

The Brady's Rocks Loop has a kind of intimate seclusion, made more intimate and more secluded by the way the rocks obscure the view as I walk among them. It's a good place to begin feeling connected to the Niagara Escarpment. I'm aware of what lies before me, in the long arc across Wisconsin, Michigan, Ontario, and New York, what kinds of outcroppings and cliff faces I will see, what kinds of heights I will need to ascend to reach the cuesta, how some masses of rock will make me feel insignificant when I stand at their bases. I'm pleased to have ambled around so circumscribed a space, getting up close and personal with the Escarpment on what almost seems a human scale. I'll savor it as I continue down the Ice Age Trail, eager to see what's ahead of me.

2

In Wisconsin, the Niagara Escarpment is often called the Ledge and Ledge County Park is named for a prominent stretch of it. My first visit in September found the park busy with campers and picnickers. Parking near access to a scenic overlook, I walked through a narrow stretch of woods to the lip of the ledge and its limited open vistas. Only from a few places could I look across country homes and farms to distant Horicon Marsh State Wildlife Refuge, roughly 300 feet lower in elevation, see the glimmerings of water, and scan expansive flatness in every direction.

Walking south along the trail through a narrow strip of woods, I stepped out to the lip of the Ledge from time to time, hoping for a view of the height and composition of the Ledge itself. When the trail veered away from the edge, I ambled into the trees and discovered crevices underfoot, some barely noticeable, some too large to step or even leap across. At the scarp face, fractures in the rock widen due to weathering, the impact of water from rain and snow freezing and expanding in the cracks; those separations will, over time, begin to lean and eventually topple. The Ledge here ranges from 30 to 50 feet high and the crevices are often narrow, dark, and deep.

On Lower Ledge Road, a well-tended lawn was alive with picnickers and the understory of the woods camouflaged the base of the scarp. The Contemplation Tree, a large lopsided oak at the edge of the woods, limbs stretching mostly west, harbored three widely spaced benches behind it in the shade. It looked inviting, though with the activity nearby, perhaps challenging, as well. Driving slowly, I located trailheads that promised places to explore in the woods when I returned.

Now in early November I find Lower Ledge Road blocked, the campgrounds closed for the season. I'm the only one in the park. I park, take the familiar path toward the Ledge, and within five steps, trip and fall flat on the ground. I'm glad I'm not near the edge of the Ledge. Fallen leaves cover the trail, hiding a surface often uneven, rocky and root-strewn. It's an overcast day and the view of Horicon Marsh is vague and undefined. I walk north this time, the trail running close to the edge, the forest deep and thick, and visible precipices stark and high and seldom as fractured as in the southern stretch. Birdsong is plentiful, but no birds appear, and only a few ground squirrels dash across the trail. The forest on the cuesta is bright with yellow maple leaves, but enough leaves having fallen in the understory and below the Ledge, it's easy to step onto one prominence and see the cliff face below a neighboring one. Many of the prominences actually *are* ledges, their lower levels eroded away, their tops protruding shelves. Occasionally I spot a cave—some said to be 15-to-20-feet deep—in the center or at the base of the scarp.

A set of steps leads to the lower level. The trail bypasses the base of the cliffs and drops down to Lower Ledge Road. I stride across the flat lawn searching for a trail heading into the woods and pass the Contemplation Tree without pausing to contemplate. A trail lets me see the face of the Ledge and, uncertain what's under thick layers of leaves, I climb slowly through the trees. From below, the exposed Ledge reveals a jagged surface, a series of rock layers unevenly weathered, like a ragged stack of bricks or Lego blocks. It's like approaching a mismatched, misaligned row of stone towers or turrets, each in a range of brown or gray shades, darkest at the top, lightest at the bottom. Some maples growing at the top of the talus slope, tight against the base of the towers, have now surpassed them in height. One tree anchored in a crevice at the bottom of a tower has an exposed mass of sturdy, tangled roots.

I notice a less precipitous section with a more continuous slope, veer toward it and clamber back to the top, happy to complete the circuit on my own and feeling better acquainted with the Ledge.

* * *

Niagaran strata is the bedrock below everything between Brady's Rocks, close to the Kettle Moraine in Waukesha County, and Ledge Park, roughly 45 miles due north and distant from the moraine in Dodge County. I wonder why the Escarpment is exposed at Ledge Park rather than its bedrock extending further west, where its sediments were once formed. Looking out on flatlands leading up to and including Horicon Marsh, the connection between the marsh and the ledge seems remote, but the geological history of the two suggests that they were intimately involved with one another.

Horicon Marsh's history begins with glaciers. The Green Bay Lobe scraped down the west side of the Door Peninsula and created a wide lowland extending from Green Bay as far south as Illinois. When the Wisconsin Ice Sheet receded, a recessional moraine dammed what is now the Rock River and formed Glacial Green Lake. Over time the river eroded through the dam and emptied the lake, leaving a vast wetlands area. Human habitation there dates back nearly 12,000 years; Increase Lapham found more than 90 burial mounds on and around that recessional moraine. For Native Americans the marsh offered a wealth of wild rice, fish, and waterfowl.

European-Americans made it a site of constant change. Building the city of Horicon, they obliterated the mounds, then built a dam to raise the marsh's water level, and then removed the dam when farmlands flooded. In the early twentieth century, after extensively ditching and draining the marsh for more farmland and exposing peat on the marsh floor, peat fires ravaged the ecosystem. In 1927, thanks to Louis Radke and the Izaak Walton League, the Horicon Marsh State Wildlife Area was established; in 1941 the Horicon Marsh National Wildlife Refuge added an area double that size. At 33,000 acres, Horicon Marsh is one of the largest wildlife marshes in the country and a major stopover site for migrating birds. At a Milwaukee Audubon Society conference, Bill Volkert, Naturalist Emeritus at the refuge, explained that, though private clubs and commercial businesses depleted the marsh's once extensive duck popu-lation, it now supports a large geese population, who don't feed in the marsh but fly off to neighboring fields—loss for specialists is a gain for generalists, he claimed. Wendy Woyczik, a wildlife biologist, later spoke about white peli-cans at Horicon, who nest on spoil bank islands (dredging remnants) and cooperatively herd fish to shallows where they can scoop them up (rather than diving as brown pel-icans do). The marsh is still thoroughly managed, using impoundments to cycle areas through drought and flood stages. It's been recognized as a Wetland of International Importance, a Globally Important Bird Area, and an Ice Age

National Science Reserve. Through it still flows the Rock River, with a 3,600 square mile watershed and a 300-mile journey through southern Wisconsin and northwest Illinois to the Mississippi River.

The marsh, 13.5 miles long and 3-5 miles wide, provides parking areas around its perimeter for bird watching, some with anchored spotting scopes. *Important Bird Areas of Wisconsin* claims the marsh welcomes up to 250,000 geese and 100,000 assorted ducks during migration season as well as a host of other waterfowl and land birds in such varied terrain as conifer swamp, upland hardwood forest, and shrub wetlands. I can't find reliable figures on the number of bird-watchers who migrate seasonally to the marsh.

The best time to do some birding wouldn't be on an overcast early November afternoon. At the Horicon Marsh National Wildlife Refuge Headquarters, I gaze through binoculars mounted on posts across cattails and open pools of water and see only grasses buffeted by a cold wind. Inside the center, browsing a collection of paper cranes to select a few for grandchildren interested in origami, I hear a ranger tell another visitor where young whooping cranes are hanging out with sandhill cranes rather than following other whoopers south and where tundra swans, trumpeter swans, and slow-to-migrate white pelicans have been sighted. Chances to see birds close to the road are diminished, she says, when too much traffic noise drives the birds toward more isolated locations—she advises rolling down the car windows before stopping.

Driving close to the refuge, I appreciate the sprawling vastness of the marshlands. On a busy highway, as eighteen-wheelers roar by, I notice dark figures on open water and lower my windows as I slow down. From the north shoulder I scan the geese-filled vista near the south side, the water gleaming a light blue gray under cloudy skies, flotillas floating calmly across it. More geese settle into the water and more trucks whiz by, shaking my car and cutting off my view. Then I notice, where the water is shallow near the marsh grasses beyond the geese, other, taller, lighter figures: sandhill cranes. I search among them for a whooping crane or two, but maybe these aren't the bunch they've socialized with. It's hard to count the cranes in the tall grass as they continually stoop and bend for food, but I estimate at least fifteen or more are there. It takes me awhile to notice that far beyond them in the east the skyline is uniformly lined with highlands. All this time I've been looking back at the elevation formed by the Ledge. At once the relationship of Ledge and Marsh is clear to me.

* * *

Oakfield Ledge State Natural Area is about fifteen miles due north of Ledge Park, 65 miles due north of Brady's Rocks, and 50 miles due west of Lake Michigan. Locating them alters my sense of what lies beneath eastern Wisconsin. If I ever thought of the Niagara Escarpment as simply a jagged discontinuous cliff face, I don't anymore—its cuesta has assumed an enduring presence in my mind.

Wisconsin State Natural Areas preserve some aspect of a natural community like an oak savanna or prairie or bogs, fens, swamps, and woods, as well as geological formations like caves, cliffs, bluffs, waterfalls, gorges, and, as here at Oakfield Ledge, sections of the Niagara Escarpment. Unlike state and county parks, natural areas are set up for preservation and restoration, not for recreation, and offer few facilities or none. Where Ledge Park has a sprawling campground and picnic areas, restrooms, playgrounds, paved roads, and benches near scenic vistas, Oakfield Ledge has only a couple small gravel parking lots easy to overlook on the roadside and footpaths maintained by visitor use alone. The natural areas give visitors a sense of what pre-settlement Wisconsin was like in its undeveloped, untransformed state. It's easier to acquire that sense in some areas than in others.

The Oakfield Ledge Natural Area has two widely separated sections. The Ledge itself runs between and beyond the preserved sections in the natural area, coming up from the southwest and heading northeast until, just south of Oakfield, it veers east. On a satellite image the arc of trees in a mostly open landscape traces the Ledge clearly; on a topographic map tight rows of contour lines show both the Ledge's location and its steepness, a 50-foot change in elevation. Though the trees and the contour lines are continuous, the boundary lines of the state natural area's two distinct sections are not.

In September, heading for the parking lot on Breakneck Road at the southern end of the site, I drive past an exposed section of the Ledge close to the road. The lot is past an intersection with another road where new houses perch on a sheer cliff wall of perhaps 75 to 100 feet, above an extensively mined quarry.

Once through the grass and into the woods—basswood, sugar maple, slippery elm, mountain maple, shagbark hickory, and Canada yew, according to the guidebook *Wisconsin Naturally*—the trail diverges into two, one heading close along the cliff face, another further away through the woods. I head to the scarp. Ferns abound, walking fern, fragile fern, and cliff brake, as at Brady's Rocks, as well as rare rock whitlow grass and "rare terrestrial snails," of which I see no sign. Weathering has formed extensive crevices and fractures in the Ledge, the foremost blocks separated from the blocks behind. At first, I can stand on one prominence and view a straight precipice nearby, at least 40 feet high, but further north I find gaps between the rocks the trail crosses and the leading Ledge portions. The underbrush is thick and overgrown. Stepping gingerly over narrow cracks nearing the edge, I soon face wide crevasses I can't leap across, their bottoms deep, sometimes dark, and always jumbled with rocky debris under a thick coating of fallen leaves. I move slowly, peering cautiously over the edge, aware that I could climb down into some crevices. State Natural Areas don't provide handy staircases or trail markers like formal parks do; anyone venturing into the crevices is entirely on his own. Alone here, I'll do nothing for which I'd regret not having a companion.

Up ahead, I first hear two young women discuss climbing into a gap and then a change in their voices suggests they've begun a descent. I search for the likely opening, then start going down a wide crevice that gets narrower and cooler as it deepens. When I see the women's backs below, I halloo them cheerily, hoping not to startle them, and ask how far it goes. "A long way," one of them says, and the other adds, "Maybe to the bottom." It seems impolite to follow them, so I tell them where I am is far enough down for me and advise them to yell loudly if they need help. They are at least 20 feet below the lip of the surface, angling lower toward a darker section of the fracture where a bend will take them out of sight; if the rocks that have separated from the Ledge are far enough apart and have separated completely, they may make it to the base of the formation. They may even see some rare terrestrial snails.

Climbing easily out of the gap into dappled sunlight, I stay on the path along the edge. Blocks and blocks of the Niagara cuesta have weathered through and separated from the main formation and blocks and blocks more are in various stages of weathering to reach the same result. Where grass or moss or ferns hang over the fractures, it would be easy to step into one.

About a mile farther, the path becomes less open and obvious. At the southern section's limit, I turn back to follow the path further from the edge, easier and more open and crossing smaller fractures. I hear the women's voices again and spot one of them a little distance away, standing on an edge and calling below her. Her companion must be at the base of the Ledge or ascending a different crevice than the one I saw them in. The exploring has gone well for them.

In a more limited way perhaps, it's also gone well for me. I'm getting a clearer image of the Escarpment and the Cuesta in and beyond my part of Wisconsin, both above and below ground.

In November I return to walk the northern section. Driving north past open fields, I find a small dirt parking area, surrounded by tall brown grasses near the trees. At an opening where grass has been trodden, I follow a trail veering toward a forest to the north. Almost as soon as I enter the trees, I feel the terrain change and notice weathered rocks underfoot, the top of the Niagara cuesta.

The forest is bright with maple leaves, interspersed occasionally with a few older, more expansive oaks. Unlike the trail in the southern section, this path doesn't go near the edge of the Ledge. The woods are generally thick and overgrown; few places invite me deeper in. Soon the trail leaves the woods and runs in the grasses. When the path turns south, I leave it to cut across the forest floor to an open space above a wide, deep, rectangular quarry, long grass disguising its edge. The walls are sheer; grasses, shrubs, and trees are reclaiming the floor. Beyond quarry walls to the west, I see farmland stretching out below and the haze above distant Horicon Marsh. Stepping into the woods, I see a clearer face of the Ledge, but no easy access to follow the lip. Somewhere near here should be the remains of a limestone kiln and a spring and a clay pit but no paths seem to lead to them, the woods too thick and overgrown to search.

On the way back, glimpses of sky through trees suggest that woods are less deep there and the edge of the Ledge possibly close. I venture into them and find, as along the southern stretch, fractured, deep, narrow gashes or wide abysses between the main escarpment and blocks that lean or simply stand away from it. Here both the outliers and the leading edge are thickly moss covered, often grassy right up to the brink, and the footing demands attentiveness. The trees below the Ledge are tall enough and the woods dense enough that I have little sense of the drop-off until I'm right at its rim. I gaze into the darknesses at the bottom of the deepest crevices and note the way they suggest further, darker depths. I try to imagine the amount of time it took for relentless changes of season, the weathering of rain and ice and freeze and thaw, to separate these blocks of rock from one another. But I only imagine myself imagining it—my imagination, supported by my meager knowledge, is in no way sufficient to the task.

As I turn back toward the path, a hairy woodpecker flits among the trees, minding his own business, the only bird I've seen this morning. I leave him to his chores and retrace my steps to the parking lot. Just as I seem to have reached the limit of the Oakfield Ledge, rain begins and sends me to my car and home, to contemplate the map of the arc of the Escarpment that's starting to unfold in my mind.

3

The meandering scarp marking the border between lowlands and cuesta uplands extends northeast from Oakfield toward Fond du Lac and arches around the eastern shore of Lake Winnebago, the "lac" whose southern "fond" gives the city its name. A driver coming up from the southwest and rounding southern Lake Winnebago could rise onto the cuesta and cross it all the way to Manitowoc, on the shore of Lake Michigan. Glaciers shaped that landscape.

Horicon Marsh, Lake Winnebago, and Green Bay occupy much of the lowlands at a southwest-northeast angle, roughly bordered by the Niagara Escarpment. Glacial ice sheets gouged out the lowlands and rubbed against the cuesta uplands. Over millennia, meltwater behind recessional moraines of the advancing and receding Green Bay lobe created large glacial lakes. After the Rock River drained Glacial Green Lake, the wetlands that became Horicon Marsh remained. Further north, fluctuations between 15,000 and 13,000 years ago repeatedly formed and covered and reformed Glacial Lake Oshkosh and its varied outlets. At one time the lake drained southwest, down a unified flowage headed toward the Mississippi. Further glacial melting exposed a low subcontinental divide that turned that single outlet into two rivers, the Wisconsin heading west and south and the Fox flowing east into Lake Oshkosh. As the glacier receded north, lake outlets flowed toward what became

Lake Michigan, first through the Manitowoc River and then through more northerly rivers. Eventually Glacial Lake Oshkosh was gone, Lake Winnebago was left behind, and the Fox River that flowed into it midway up the west side also flowed out of its northwest corner down into Green Bay.

According to Rachel Krebs Paull, Glacial Lake Oshkosh's surface was 65 feet higher than the surface of contemporary Lake Winnebago and the Niagara Escarpment rose on Lake Oshkosh's eastern shore at less height than it now rises above Lake Winnebago. Today Lake Winnebago is the largest lake in Wisconsin, 28 miles long, 8 miles wide, encompassing around 137,500 acres and bordered by three counties. Its greatest depth is 21 feet and its average depth is roughly 15 feet. Fishermen come for walleye, white bass, yellow perch, and, in ice fishing season, sturgeon. The lake is dotted with boats in warm weather and with trucks, snow-mobiles, and ice-fishing shanties when ice-covered. Now a site for sport and play, it offers a few reminders of its role in Wisconsin's history.

Jean Nicolet, the first European to enter Wisconsin, landed on the shore of *"la baie verte"* in 1634. He and some Hurons canoed from Mackinac Island in Lake Huron through the Straits of Mackinac and along the northern shore of Lake Michigan. In Green Bay he connected with the Ho-Chunk, canoed up the lower Fox River into Lake Winnebago, then followed the upper Fox River to a portage into the Wisconsin River and navigated further, hoping to reach the Pacific Ocean. Having established contact between the French and Ouisconsin's native peoples, Nicolet returned to Quebec. In 1673, Pere Jacques Marquette and Louis Joliet retraced Nicolet's route up the Fox and down the Wisconsin, reaching the Mississippi River at what is now

Prairie du Chien and descending the Mississippi south to the mouth of the Arkansas River. The connection they established between Green Bay and the Mississippi opened up a promising fur trade route, and eventually trading posts were built at either end of the portage. In 1828, an American fort, Fort Winnebago, was constructed on the Fox River end of the portage; it was the setting for *Wau-bun, The Early Day in the Northwest* by Juliette Kinzie, who lived there from 1830-1834 with her Indian agent husband. Over decades the city of Portage grew up around the fort.

After countless centuries of Native American use and two hundred years of European-American passage, the Fox-Wisconsin waterway was subjected to "improvement." On the upper Fox, a linking canal was constructed between 1837 and 1876; on the lower Fox, dams and locks were installed over substantial rapids between Lake Winnebago and Green Bay. Reuben Gold Thwaites canoed the Fox in 1887, observing, in *Down Historic Waterways*, that, due to the success of railroads, "the canal, like most of the Fox and Wisconsin river-improvement, is fast relapsing into a relic." "River-improvement" raised the water level of Lake Winnebago three feet, making it larger than the lake the glaciers left behind.

The Niagara Escarpment spoons around the southern and eastern sides of Lake Winnebago, nearby quarries taking advantage of the Ledge. The Wisconsin Department of Transportation planned to reroute a highway to climb the Ledge more northerly, but a concerted community challenge to preserve Indian mounds prevented it. The Escarpment is a reminder of geologic history here, the mounds a reminder of cultural history. Both are often overlooked in our culture's preoccupation with development and commerce.

Northbound State Highway 55 rises onto the Ledge and a sideroad leads to Stockbridge Ledge Woods State Natural Area, a 43-acre forested site roughly 200 feet higher than the highway. The escarpment falls away from the flat cuesta in easy, barely noticeable stages except for one precipitous fifty-foot descent halfway down. The natural area is centered more on woods than on ledge, with a mature forest, a diverse understory, and a view of distant Lake Winnebago. Just south of it, a large, partly water-filled quarry indicates that Escarpment dolostone is nearby.

A few miles further north the Escarpment veers west closer to the shore of the lake. The highway climbs the cuesta, the escarpment to the west, above the lake. The lowest portion of 200-acre Calumet County Park is on the Winnebago shore; the highest portion is on the Escarpment with exposed sections of the Ledge trending north-northeast. In winter one slope is reserved for tubing, with cross-country skiing and snowmobiling encouraged; in summer trails are open to mountain biking and campgrounds are near a boat launch and beach. The park also maintains six effigy mounds on top of the escarpment.

* * *

Geology and culture come together memorably at High Cliff State Park, between both a stretch of Lake Winnebago shoreline and a parallel stretch of Escarpment. Effigy mounds are concentrated on the escarpment, surrounded by a self-guided loop trail accessible from a family campground to the south, a roadside parking area to the north, and a hiking trail to the west following the scarp. The Red Bird Trail runs from an observation tower past a 12-foot-high bronze statue of the Winnebago (Ho-Chunk) chief Red Bird, through a quarry, past the Indian mounds and the campground to nearly the southern border of the park. Red Bird's raids on white miners and boatmen along the Mississippi in 1827 led to the Ho-Chunk ceding the lead mining region of Wisconsin to the federal government and to the construction of Fort Winnebago. Standing in the midst of picnic areas, scenic overlooks, and parking lots, the statue seems an anomalous feature. Yet it does remind visitors that, for centuries before European settlement, Native Americans looked out over the lake and the lowlands, occupied the cliffs above them, and built both conical and effigy burial mounds on the cuesta.

In 1851, for his book *The Antiquities of Wisconsin*, Increase Lapham sailed across the lake from Menasha "to examine and survey the mounds on the top of a high limestone cliff or ledge." He found three long mounds in "a small clearing on the bank of the lake, not far from the foot of the bluff," and "three small embankments, extending across a small ridge from the bank of the lake to a valley back of it." Lapham and his companions climbed the ledge with "much difficulty," claiming it had "quite a formidable aspect" and was "probably two hundred feet high above the water; the last forty or fifty being perpendicular, or nearly so." On the top, he found "an almost level plateau, extending towards the east" and a "magnificent view of the lake and surrounding country." He observed, "Those who have examined the banks of the Niagara below the great falls, or the mountain ridge as is seen in western New York and Canada, will have a correct idea of this ledge of limestone"; as it was "composed of a rock of the same geological age, the resemblance is not to be wondered at." His illustration, Plate XLI, highlights a "Perpendicular Cliff of Limestone 200 feet high" above Lake Winnebago and a series of sometimes widely separated effigy mounds along the top. An inset section of the plate shows a similar site some five miles away, "where the main ledge is further back from the lake and is much less steep." Though "tormented by mosquitoes" and the forest's damp heat, he nonetheless felt that the "land along the east shore of Lake Winnebago is among the finest in the state" and "just such land as would be selected by an agricultural people."

As early as 1836, Lapham had called attention to Indian mounds in Wisconsin, writing about "the existence of the 'turtle-mound' at Prairie Village, now Waukesha, and of other animal effigies at various places." He continued to survey mounds and enlisted the Smithsonian Institution in an effort to record and preserve them. Though his efforts "not unfrequently saved from oblivion" some mounds, often "they were destroyed immediately or within a few days after my survey." *The Antiquities of Wisconsin*, published in 1855, is a record of a prodigious effort to locate as many existing mounds as possible as well as a testament to how much of that cultural history has been obliterated by agriculture, industry, and civic enterprise.

The practice of mound building in Wisconsin dates back as far as 800 B.C.E.; animal- or spirit-shaped effigy mounds were especially important between 800 and 1200 C.E. An estimated 15,000 to 20,000 mounds, at over 900 separate centers, existed here at the time of European-American settlement. Some 4,000 still exist, belatedly protected by the state's Burial Sites Protection Law, passed in 1985. Most mounds were conical, oval, or linear, but many took effigy shapes. Arguing for a complex ceremonial significance to design and placement, Robert A. Birmingham and Leslie E. Eisenberg, in *Indian Mounds of Wisconsin*, write that "effigy mound groups are maps of ancient belief structures," what the anthropologist R. Clark Mallam termed an "ideology from the earth."

Birmingham and Eisenberg observe that "the orientation and arrangement of mounds often follow the contours of the landform on which they were built, apparently artistically inspired by the topography." Effigies shaped like birds or men, usually found on ridge tops, represented the upper-world; those shaped as animals—bear or buffalo, wolf or fox, deer or elk—represented the earth portion of the lower world; and water spirits, long-tailed forms often identified as panthers or turtles or lizards, placed near water sources and more prevalent in southeastern Wisconsin, represented the water portion. The High Cliff site contains conical mounds, a linear mound, two mounds identified as "Twin Buffaloes" and four designated as "panther-shaped" (likely water spirits, given the location overlooking Lake Winnebago). High Cliff is an ideal place to celebrate sky, earth, and water.

The Indian Mound Trail loops past low mounds, their shapes hard to discern. In spring and summer ground cover is abundant, and in autumn the forest floor is densely layered with leaves of white oak, shagbark hickory, and basswood. White-breasted nuthatches, downy woodpeckers, chicka-dees, and black and gray squirrels abound. The mounds are easy to lose track of in the woods. These few mounds are only a small sample of the multitude destroyed by settlers, farmers, and quarrymen; the nearby family campground occupies a site where once there may have been other mounds or Indian encampments. But with a stretch of the imagination, it might be possible to envision what the view on the top of the Escarpment at High Cliff was like a few hundred years ago.

* * *

Approaching High Cliff State Park on a May morning, I circle down off the Niagara cuesta toward a large scallop of water in the northeast corner of Lake Winnebago. Past the park entrance, at an intersection with the park's main road, I locate a marina with over a hundred slips to my right and a playground, picnic shelters, a bathhouse, and a beach straight ahead. To my left, the road leads past a mid-nineteenth century brick General Store serving as a combination museum/visitor center. Beyond it the road forks, a short branch heading toward the Old Lime Kiln Ruins, a longer one leading up the Escarpment and through the quarry that fed the kilns. Twenty-first century recreation and nineteenth-century industrial history co-exist here, and mounds secluded on the cliffs give quiet evidence of an even deeper cultural history.

Between 1856 and 1956, the Western Lime and Cement Company occupied the site. A company town, complete with houses, taverns, a school, and a church, stood here, with a dance hall and amusement park up on the cliffs and frequent traffic from towns across the lake. Dolomite quarried from the cliffs was fed into kilns below for limestone, the clay in Maquoketa shale underlying the Silurian strata was used in brick manufacture, and crushed rocks went off for buildings and roadbeds. Shipping barrels were manufactured on site and eventually the forests that so impressed Increase Lapham as "difficult to penetrate without the aid of an axeman" were gone. The quarrying operation closed in 1956 and the state took possession of the land for the park. Only the General Store, the Old Lime Kiln Ruins, and, of course, the quarry remain as evidence of that era.

I park and walk to the Old Lime Kiln Ruins, a broad, flat, open area, the lake visible through the trees, the shoreline hidden down a steep slope. The lime kiln ruins stretch out behind steel fencing, high, topless stone structures with further foundations terraced higher up the slope. The scale of the kilns, a high tower, and the remains of the cooper's shop close by is intimidating. Now starlings and swallows nest on the heights and swoop out over the forest and the shoreline.

From the southern end of the ruins, the Lime Kiln Trail follows the lakeside, generally inaccessible due to thick undergrowth and a short steep descent with no beach. The path is generally level, its mocha-colored soil often damp and muddy, easy to slip or slide on. The upslope on the inland side is steep and well wooded, the forest having renewed itself in the decades since the park was founded.

The trail divides into a loop. I stay on the path closer to the lake to enter the park section designated as the High Cliff Escarpment State Natural Area, running more than a mile along the shoreline on the talus slope of the Escarpment and encompassing the Indian Mounds Trail on the cuesta. Cottonwoods and willows dominate the lakeside edge of the natural area and the slopes leading further inland are well forested with ash, elm, sugar maple, and basswood. Where the trail loops away from the shoreline, I pause to gaze at the lake's ruffled blue waters and scan its distant shoreline on the western horizon. A powerboat roars past and beyond it glides a single sailboat.

The trail winds upwards over high railroad tie steps and passes through some aged and immense older trees in the midst of much younger ones. The climb is persistent and meandering, but soon the rocky face of the Escarpment emerges up ahead, rising behind and sometimes above the trees. Where the talus slope ends, trees often grow close to the base of the scarp and stretch upwards, obscuring a view of it. Sometimes the leading edge of the Escarpment is shattered and the horizontal layers of stone pitched at an angle, depending on where under layers had eroded away and weakened support of upper layers. In places, shallow crevasses or alcove-like caves are weathered into the cliff face.

When the trail seems about to lead right into the Escarpment, it arches around a massive, nearly square pillar, some thirty uneven layers thick, leaning slightly toward the talus. Between the pillar and the intact scarp a passage leads to a wooden staircase that takes me to the top of the Ledge and out onto the Red Bird Trail and access to the Indian Mounds Loop. I walk north along the Escarpment's edge. Up here the weathering is often pronounced; blocks of stone are separated from one another, gaps between them sometimes shallow, sometimes deep. I step out onto one promontory and survey a neighboring one, noting the height of the cliff face and the extent to which the topmost layers have been undercut down to the talus. Some cliffs are said to be 25 feet high or more and, as elsewhere, they host unique plant

life—fragile fern, bulbet fern, cliff stickseed, long-beaked sedge. I step carefully near the edge, wary of hidden fractures and uneven surfaces. Trees of every size have rooted themselves in the slimmest of cracks, often seeming to grow out of bare rock.

Back at the stairs, I survey that freestanding pillar again, the regular placement of its layers, the apparent tabletop flatness of its uppermost layer, the way it leans away from the scarp across the path. Descending, I gaze at rock walls towering over me, thinking about how long it took to lay down all those layers of sediment, turn them into dolostone, cover them with more layers of sediment and then wear that sediment away, scrape them with glaciers, and erode them by means of rain, snow, ice, and wind so that they stand as I see them now, still changing, imperceptibly but inevitably.

On the way back I take the upper portion of the loop, more uneven and demanding than the lower, to walk the higher range of the talus slope and view the escarpment's varied debris, eons of collapsed or sliding slabs hiding the bottom of the escarpment and the thick woods growing and toppling and decaying on top of them. I take my time, contented that rough footing slows my walk in the forest, pleased to delay my return to the lime kiln ruins and the populated part of the park and the roads that will take me back into the century where I live.

4

I come to Cherney Maribel Caves County Park in Manitowoc County in midsummer, recently reopened a year after an August tornado swept through, tearing up the landscape. It toppled thousands of trees in the park's 75 acres, destroyed the park shelter and restrooms, decimated the nearby remnants of a historic stone hotel, and made the park inaccessible. I expect to find a steep Silurian dolomite cliff face, the western wall of a channel carved by an outlet of Glacial Lake Oshkosh, where the West Twin River still flows, with caves said to extend well over 100 feet deep. It's also the site of the Cherney Maribel Caves State Natural Area, with a hardwood forest on the upland, cedar, hemlock, and birch on the valley floor.

Since the tornado, loggers have removed lumber and volunteers have restored damaged stairs and trails. Storm damage is starkly evident along the road winding down from the park entrance: piles of broken trees, limbs, and branches, stumps cut low to the ground, emptiness where the canopy had been, the forest floor open and exposed. The parking lot is clear and empty and the trail along the top of the bluffs smells of fresh cut wood chips. Near the stairs to the caves, it is overwhelmed by forest debris and thick summer undergrowth.

The solid staircase descends close to the bluff face. Rugged, dark layers of dolomite cap the bluff; two cedars perch at its edge, surrounded by ferns, a cave below partially hidden by jagged rocks and dark shadows. At the bottom of the stairs, I drift along a path close to the rock wall, towering 50 feet high in places, and quickly reach the locked, gated entrance to Tartarus Cave, the most developed cave in the park, inaccessible except on organized monthly tours.

Like other crevices, niches, alcoves, and indentations along the Niagara Escarpment, the Cherney Maribel caves were formed by dolomite decomposition. The freezing and thawing of water in cracks and joints, the drip of meltwater and rain, created open spaces within the rock and, where the flow of springs was strong enough, exposed them in the bluff face. Outwash from Glacial Lake Oshkosh wore through the bluff to reveal caves and niches and filled some openings. Once spelunkers explored Tartarus Cave, they discovered its potential for expansion and uncovered three entrances. The Wisconsin Speleological Society removed glacial debris, cleared interior passages to other caves, and found links to sinkholes on top of the bluff. Like the New Hope Cave at the other end of the park, also gated and under development, the nature of Tartarus Cave is in flux.

The bottom of the bluff here is clear of moss and lichen, its talus removed to accommodate the trail. Clambering up to various openings, I kneel and gaze into small caves until the path veers away from the bluff. Voices behind me, at first clear, then increasingly hollow, draw me to a low cave. I bend and peer inside. A young man sits within, filling the passage, and a woman's voice sounds more deeply inside. With his cellphone's flashlight app, he tries to lighten the side tunnel she's crawled into, but she can't tell what's ahead of her. Reluctant to go further, she backs out. They say "No, thanks," when I offer my flashlight.

We chat briefly about the cave's darkness and tightness until they notice another opening where, hunching down, we see sunlight at a tunnel's opposite end. She drops down and begins wiggling through it; he squats down to encourage her, then rises to circle round to meet her where she'll crawl out. At their first cave, I note how low and rounded the walls and ceiling are, how much bluff rises above it, how dark it gets as it angles away from the opening. I edge a little way inside, but my little flashlight is not particularly illuminating, and I slowly back out.

I head north toward the State Natural Area. The path parallels the bluffs at a little distance, the slopes below them often containing narrow streams of seepage from bluffs or caves. Where water trickles under a low bridge, I realize its jumble of stones disguises a worn path to an opening in the bluffs, Cooper's Cave, one often visited by visitors.

Cooper's Cove is identified as "a square tube solutional cave," "relatively quiet and dry," "distinguished by its large rectangular entrance." The water under the bridge, bound for the West Twin River, comes from a natural spring emerging from the talus some nine feet below the entrance. The cave is said to be about 20 feet deep with two bigger, higher rooms. With some caution—the rocks are often slick though dry and angled rather than flat, some rounded, some jagged—I climb toward the cave.

The entrance is somewhat narrow and, a few steps in, veers away to the right. Remembering the promise of larger rooms, I stoop and duckwalk a little way deeper into a bigger space, one I can't stand up in but doesn't trigger claustrophobia. Beyond the larger room a smaller tunnel leads deeper in. Suddenly remembering a daunting cave scene in Nevada Barr's mystery *Blind Descent*, where ranger Anna Pigeon relies only on touch and memory to escape pitch blackness, I duckwalk slowly out and step carefully over the rocks to the boardwalk at the base of the slope.

The tour map displays specific sites a guide might point out, but everywhere the undergrowth is dense with fallen trees, piles of lopped-off limbs, and trunks chainsawed through to clear the path and prevent more collapses. Sometimes the bluffs are hard to see from the path. I try to scan joints and fractures and overhanging slabs, the broken off sections at the base, cedars perched exactly on the lip or hanging off the edge, places where crevasses might be widening gradually into caves, the mass of stone rising above the trail. Bare spaces at bluff top show where trees were ripped away; debris below them sports undergrowth in the unfamiliar presence of sunlight. Everywhere there is an abundance of ferns and moss. I see no birds and hear no birdsong. I climb to the entrance to Pancake Cave, high on the bluff line, fallen rock around the entrance and access difficult, even a little treacherous, over a rugged talus slope. I peek inside, but don't try to enter.

I soon reach Maribel New Hope Cave, the principal tour cave. A few benches and a wide, open space front it. The cave was unknown until someone noticed steam rising from a talus pile on a cold winter day. Rocks were removed to reveal a small opening. Wisconsin Speleological Society members cleared interior passages until, after "a two-foot-high belly crawl," they found a larger cave room. Since 2004, cavers have diligently excavated New Hope Cave, lowered the floor of the entrance and made it accessible to tourists.

I take an unmarked side trail in search of one last cave. At the end of a boardwalk and observation platform in considerable disrepair I see the gated entrance to Spring

Cave, barely visible at the base of the bluff through the foliage. It has a natural spring the old hotel once used for its therapeutic outdoor baths and bottling plant. The spring water gurgles down the slope, but I can get no closer.

Back on the top of the bluff, after following a path into an overgrown and lumber-littered area, I opt to head home. Remembering that couple crawling in those caves and having peered into many quarries and crevasses and walked along and beneath and up and down a lot of bluffs, I wonder what sense of the Escarpment I would have if I really got inside it.

* * *

From Door County to the Illinois state line, the Niagara Cuesta is riddled with karst features, where weathering dissolves bedrock to form joints and fractures, grikes and clints, worn and grooved by the acidic composition of groundwater and rainwater that puddle and flow across them, seep into them, and freeze, expand, thaw, and drain. Scarp edge crevasses and fractures wear away passages in soluble material below, creating underground streams, carving subterranean passages, and sculpting solution caves exposed in cliffs by collapsing rock faces.

When cave roofs grow thinner, the weight of unsupported rock collapses them, forming sinkholes (or dolines). A sink can be a shallow depression, barely noticeable to a passerby, or an immense opening in the ground. Sometimes, sinkholes open unexpectedly below populated areas, swallowing houses, cars, parking lots, and people; during rainy spring planting, tractors sometimes fall into a sink.

On the surface the ground may seem solid enough, a cave roof still intact or a sinkhole layered over by glacial debris. In eastern Wisconsin glaciers covered karst terrain, and till and outwash filled sinkholes to sometimes great depths, but further north, glacial covering is thinner, making sinkholes easier to locate and, in some cases, to excavate and explore.

Sinkholes vary in shape, size, and depth. They may be enclosed depressions, low spots in the landscape; they may be deeper, funnel shaped depressions where upper levels widen as bottom levels sink deeper; they may be subsidence sinkholes, where soil that once covered the hole has washed into an underground cavity; they may be collapsed sinkholes, with steep sides, where overlying rock has dropped into a subterranean cave. Without excavation or exploration, it's hard to know how vast the openings below a sinkhole may be or how horizontal, vertical, or sinuous underground passages may be.

Karst terrain can be problematic when groundwater enters into aquifers and water supplies and moves rapidly along dolostone fractures. As Dott and Attig point out, "A septic system, an area where farm animals are concentrated, or a parking lot, if placed over a solution-widened fracture, may contaminate water moving hundreds to thousands of feet through the ground in only a few days to a place where it is pumped from a well." Pollution also enters streams and springs, affecting endangered species in the Escarpment's restricted environment.

In karst terrain the water flow along fractures can carve out substantial surface channels, such as major valleys on the Door Peninsula. The West Twin River inherited the Glacial Lake Oshkosh outwash channel, flowed past Cherney Maribel Caves and its outwash-scraped bluffs, and exposed solution caves already formed in the cuesta. They aren't the only solution caves accessible through sinkholes in the cuesta's karst terrain.

* * *

Arriving early for a cave tour at Ledge View Nature Center, in Calumet County, I stroll through thick woods to a quarry overlook, then descend to its floor, a flat, scruffy open space with small trees, strips of grass, and shrubs scattered throughout the gravel and rock-strewn surface. The high eastern wall is uneven, but close to plumb. A few smooth, tightly compressed slabs stand out from rougher stone above and below them. In cracks and joints on higher levels, shrubs have taken root, but the wall is otherwise clear of growth. As quarries dig their way back into the cuesta, solution caves are often exposed and, if the quarrying goes on long enough, obliterated. At the Ledge View quarry, I find only one hole under a narrow ledge that might suggest a deeper cave.

Ledge View Nature Center is on a rise, above Escarpment outcroppings; its Ledge Walk Trail provides views of the Ledge on a path along the base of low bluffs. The quarry offers sense of the depth of the cuesta here—in eastern Wisconsin Niagaran strata can be between 347 and 652 feet thick and this quarry wall is only some fifty feet high, suggesting what might lie beneath the till thinly coating the bedrock.

At the Nature Center I meet Jane Mingari, the naturalist who will give only me the tour—no one else has signed up—and tell her about my Escarpment project. She out-fits herself in rubber boots and water-resistant outerwear. I assure her I'm dressed to get muddy and dirty in the caves—old clothes, frayed pants, beat-up sweatshirt, hiking shoes, and a baseball cap with a small attached flashlight.

Along the half-mile walk to the cave, Jane reminds me we're treading on cave roofs and points out a barely noticeable off-trail depression, covered with leaves and undergrowth, where a cavity has formed below it.

We descend a sunlit staircase to a heavy metal door installed to reduce frost damage (and random exploring), the main entrance to Carolyn's Caverns, at over 700 feet one of the longest cave systems in eastern Wisconsin. Once out of sight of that doorway our only light in the cave will be flashlights.

The first room, the Bat Room, is spacious and easy to stand in. Big brown bats, little brown bats, long-eared bats, and tri-colored bats (eastern pipistrelles) live in the caves, entering and exiting through an opening in the steel door. Only one will flash by us later. During winter bat hibernation the caves are closed.

Jane lets me explore two side rooms, squirming on my belly in and out of one passage and clambering down into a deep enclosed space with a muddy bottom. Then we wander through the caves. I step carefully, wary of overhead protrusions, often bending, stooping, crawling on hands and knees, or outright slithering. Only one place is especially tight, less so for Jane than for me. Longer crawls through passages like the Whale's Throat and the Kid's Passage mean venturing into long dark holes unable to raise my head or propel myself

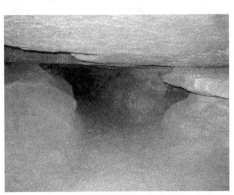

by any means other than elbows and thighs. I pay strict attention to where I am.

At Carolyn's Cave, the original entrance to the system 17 feet below the surface. Jane shows me where a waterfall had been and we descend a double set of ladders to the bottom of Dave's Sink, the deepest part of the system, nearly four stories or 36 feet deep. One smooth trough shows the direction of the waterfall flow. A wall composed of concretized glacial outwash fills a deep sinkhole that predated the glacier. On the other side of the sinkhole is Mother's Cave, a separate system that would link to Carolyn's Caverns if the sinkhole were excavated. The Wisconsin Speleological Society have facilitated access to the caves here, discovering entrances and excavating mud and debris. At times, peering down a dark passage, I imagine crawling in to see just how far it would take me, how tangled and interconnected the cavities might be.

Everywhere along the Ledge layers upon layers of deposition vary in density and composition. Geologists sorting out depositional history identify subdivisions of strata from the Precambrian Era through Cambrian, Ordovician, Silurian, and Devonian Periods. The most recent, Devonian, is missing throughout most of eastern Wisconsin, and Silurian strata most immediately underlies glacial depositions. In a stratigraphic column, each geologic period is subdivided into coded blocks. The Silurian in Wisconsin is principally divided, from earliest (lowest) deposition to latest (highest), into the Mayville Formation, the Burnt Bluff Group, the Manistique Formation, and the Engadine Formation, each named for a location where it was prominent. Each can be further subdivided on the basis of composition, texture, and color—the Mayville Formation, for example, is fine-to-medium grained and preserves fossils of early life forms such as corals and brachiopods, while the Burnt Bluff Group is more fine-grained, entirely dolostone, and contains fewer fossils. Some stratigraphers argue for further subdivisions based on "lithographic character," more limited and precise identifications of strata.

In Carolyn's Caverns, Jane shines her flashlight on layers of Burnt Bluff and Mayville dolomite, emphasizing the distinction between them. She locates a few fossils, such as a gastropod imbedded in the rock, and miniature stalactites on some ceilings. She points out flowstone, sheets of calcite deposits that coat some walls, often in ripples, and finds examples of chert and cave coral. She identifies lifelines, the places where the narrow but persistent penetration of water began the formation of the cave, and steers me around "hungry mud," the sticky pools on the cave floors. At times of heavy rains, the caves have been flooded, once as much as eighteen feet deep. No one knows exactly where the water goes when it drains but the hungry mud reminds everyone that it's been there.

From Dave's Sink we crawl through the Whale's Throat back to the Bat Room. I climb out while Jane locks up, then leads me to another site, Montgomery's Cave. The Carolyn's Caverns Cave System is the most often toured and most accessible of the caves at Ledge View; Mother's Cave, famous for its "big squeeze"—the tight fit that the box in the Nature Center lets visitors test their girth against— requires the most crawling, only open Saturday mornings; Montgomery's Cave, the least developed, is only toured by special groups. We descend hand over hand down one ladder into a large room with an eleven-foot-high ceiling and then, through a hole in the floor, down another ladder to a second room and a vertical depth of 30 feet. This solution cave, first discovered and explored in the 1860s, was randomly visited by local people. A rendering plant on the site used it as a refuse dump for processed horse carcasses and, after the plant burned down, for unprocessed carcasses and debris, filling the cave. Though the Department of Health made owners clean the cave, cavers sometimes find bones in remote passages and a horse's skull still rests on one ledge.

Once again, I feel the tug of unexplored passages but easily resist it. Still, I'm surprised not to feel more relieved when we leave Montgomery's Cave and re-enter open air. I've been before and upon the Niagara Escarpment and now deep within its cuesta. I feel more intimately connected with it here than perhaps anywhere else.

Whenever I drive away from somewhere on the Escarpment I retain my sense of that location by reviewing—almost as if in a video—my passage around it. Leaving Ledge View I try to keep crawling through the caves and conversating with Jane in mind, but the caves of Cherney Maribel begin to surface, as if on a split screen. The Cherney Maribel landscape makes me conscious of sudden changes on the surface, how a day's storm, a sudden tornado, obliterates decades of woodland growth and decimates what fire and decay had wrought on a century-old building, how long the forest will take to recover and the park to restore itself. But the caves of Maribel and, especially, the caves of Ledge View, which I descended to their very bottom, make me aware of what time means to the earth itself: the unimaginably slow process of constructing the cuesta, wearing away passages within it, scraping off what settled upon it over millennia and then depositing glacial debris upon it. In comparison, what fraction of the blink of an eye does my existence, these parks' existence, the devastation wrought by a few minutes in a whirlwind, take up?

5

The word "escarpment" evokes a sense of scale and precipitousness; calling the same geological feature a "ledge" downsizes and domesticates its height and verticality. In Wisconsin the Ledge names a consistently connected feature varying widely in height or exposure and calling it the Escarpment inflates its size and scale. Think of the difference in scale, the way Niagara Falls empties the waters of four Great Lakes into its gorge and the Ledge only overlooks Horicon Marsh, Lake Winnebago, and Green Bay. Nonetheless, they *are* connected, and the Wisconsin Ledge waterfalls replicate—on a smaller scale—processes that formed and maintain Niagara Falls.

Since 2010, officially designated as "the Year of the Escarpment," the Niagara Escarpment Resource Network (NERN) has been conducting its Ledge Tours. In Brown County the Escarpment parallels the Fox River on the east from Lake Winnebago to Green Bay and then continues up the east side of the bay onto the Door Peninsula. Waterfalls there carve their own substantial gorges in the cuesta.

* * *

To visit the Fonferek's Glen Conservancy Area, we board a small bus at a Park and Ride, drive on county roads, rise onto a ledge—our guide, John Luczaj, a UW-Green Bay geologist, points out it is *not* the Niagara Escarpment—and climb further. Past the main entrance, we turn onto a gravel road to follow a tree-lined lane to a clear flat space.

We disembark and walk to the edge of the gorge formed by Bower's Creek. It trickles over the lip of the falls and drops 30 feet into an olive-colored pool where mallards drift and frogs tunk. Hard Niagara dolostone at the top is undercut by chert-weakened dolostone below it. The creek's flow is barely noticeable—it will dry up later in the season, the falls dependent on spring snowmelt and occasional runoff from heavy rain. We discern thin rock layers at the falls' edge, how deeply undercut resistant layers have been. Chunks of talus line the shallow pool below the falls, the creek bed above glistening with puddles in the sunlight.

We leave the falls to cross the quarry parking area, past deceptively even-appearing rock layers in surrounding walls, then veer off into the trees to descend rocky, gravelly terrain to the creek bed. It's hard to find the creek below the rocks. The gorge floor is littered with debris that weathering and occasional flooding have dislodged from high walls. The farther downstream, the more challenging the footing. We step tentatively, checking the stability of what we step onto.

Beneath the Silurian stone layers throughout Wisconsin is the Ordovician layer of Maquoketa shale, readily observable elsewhere but here mostly buried. John invites us to feel an exposed section of Maquoketa shale, its soft muddiness the reason it's easily eroded away leaving the dolostone above it unsupported.

The gorge narrows, and the walls become higher. Light streams into a deep depression in the west wall from an opening at the top filled with gleaming blue sky. A stone arch stretches across the depression between the gorge and the hole with deeper crevices in its back wall. Near the hole's highest level a thick tree grows straight up from the vertical wall, its roots deep between stone layers. Local legend claims a cow created the hole by crashing through the depression roof, but geology indicates a more natural explanation: higher water levels—the gorge wasn't always this deep—and relentless erosion. Seeing all those stone layers we sense the amount of time it took to wear it all away.

Further downstream, a section is separating from the bluff, moving outward in one mass. A crevice little wider than a bulky man leads upward between the gorge wall and that independent block, a tree with a double trunk anchored in the talus between them, a direct if challenging passage to the bluff top.

We backtrack upstream into the quarry and out of it, hearing the sound of falling water. Last night's rain and run-off have only now reached the falls. The upsurge in the flow was well-timed, since our creekbed hiking wouldn't be so dry if we were down there now. We better appreciate what the falls are like in rainier times when Bower's Creek flows down a meandering course from Fonferek's Glen to the East River, which joins the Fox River and empties into Green Bay. Given the lightness of the flow today, I'm not sure how much of this water will make it all that way.

Aboard the bus, we circle around to Fonferek's Glen's main entrance, park near a barn—part of the conservancy's task has been to reforest agricultural land—and cross a grassy area to the low fence along the gorge. In the distance the falls are framed by thick foliage, the green of its water just another shade of the green surrounding it. Then we walk to the rim of the natural arch to look down to the creek bed and the water below. We can almost count the several stone layers holding the arch in place and the joints and fractures segmenting them. Thick grasses grow across the arch, tempting us to stroll across, but no one volunteers. We trust the geological explanation more than the local legend but conjure images of that cow stepping onto deceptively solid ground.

* * *

On a brisk but snowless March morning, the Ledge Tour will tour an area of the Door Peninsula where the Red Banks Savanna Historic District & Heritage Area might be established. At the Field Office of the U.S. Fish and Wildlife Service, Jim Uhrinak, a Land Restorationist and NERN Board Member, draws on oral history and traditional legends to map Native American migrations and explains how the Ho-Chunk, Ioway, Missouri, and Otoe tribes all connect to the Red Banks area of southeastern Green Bay, making it a significant pre-history site on the Escarpment. The area rises west to east in four steps from the coastline, with lowlands succeeded by a terrace, then by the Escarpment, and finally topped by glacial till. The soil successively varies in depth from thick to thin, the thinnest soil on the top rock surface called the alvar. The savanna that once dominated Red Banks covered some twenty acres; today only one acre survives. The Red Banks Historical District and Heritage Area would preserve what remains and restore much of what is gone. We carpool to potential sites in Brown County.

At Wequiock Falls County Park we disembark to circle the falls, its plunge pool, and its ravine. The falls are only 25 feet high, most turbulent late in winter when snowmelt increases its volume, and mostly dry by summer's end. Steven I. Dutch, University of Wisconsin-Green Bay geologist, once reported that Wequiock Falls has "retreated about 200 meters [roughly 6,562 feet or a mile and two tenths] in the 11,000 years since the ice retreated." It took 55 years for Wequiock Falls to recede one meter, while Niagara Falls averages 11 meters a year.

Still, Wequiock Falls is a good example of how river gorges are formed. Over those 11,000 years, beginning at the Escarpment and constantly deepening its plunge pool, Wequiock Creek wore away softer rock below harder surface dolostone until the unsupported rock broke off into the gorge. The creek flow seems weak now, but meltwater from a mile-high glacier was vastly more powerful in the beginning and periods of heavy rain and annual snowmelt have swollen the creek considerably. In addition, groundwater seeps through the surrounding rocks and down the walls of the ravine on either side of the falls. We see now an icy remnant of earlier seepage and photos show the entire arc of the ravine ice coated. Wequiock Falls displays the hard, gray Silurian dolostone at the top of the falls and the softer, blue Ordovician Maquoketa shale below, dug deeper into the wall. To the west the gorge continues to the lip of the Ledge, where the land slopes down toward Green Bay.

Nearby, a commemorative statue honors Jean Nicolet, who, in 1634, first made contact with Native Americans here (if not at another memorial site at Red Banks). His name appears at various locations and businesses. This statue was originally further up Highway 57 facing Green Bay; here he mostly looks at highway traffic. But it's an impressive statue, set on a base piled with slabs of dolomite, perhaps inadvertently commemorating the Wisconsin Ledge as well. Its historical marker perpetuates a more flamboyant version of his landing at the Red Banks shoreline than actually happened, claiming Nicolet appeared before the Ho-Chunk in Oriental robes, firing pistols with either hand to impress and intimidate people he assumed would be Chinese. This version is celebrated throughout Wisconsin in paintings and murals in museums and government buildings, as well as on a 1934 U.S. stamp commemorating the "Wisconsin Tercentenary." The marker repeats the legend, but the statue shows him standing calmly, looking stately, even visionary.

Our caravan leaves the county park, pauses on a side road to admire a magnificent 400-year-old oak, and then stops at Red Banks Alvar State Natural Area. An alvar is a unique environment, a flat plain of limestone or, here, dolomite either largely barren or topped by a thin soil. Images on the Internet are likely photographs from Northern Europe, usually Ireland, England, Sweden or Estonia. In North America alvars are found in Canada, particularly Ontario, and along the arc of the Niagara Escarpment, on Michigan's Drummond Island and Ontario's Manitoulin Island and Bruce Peninsula. Red Banks on the Door Peninsula is the principal alvar site in Wisconsin.

Entering a fairly dense forest of bur oak, shagbark hickory, red cedar and aspen, we're told to watch where we place our feet. Grass and fallen leaves disguise the fractured alvar surface, a system of grikes or grooves and clints, the surface sections the grikes divided—like a pretzel roll's fragmented surface. Foliage clinging to the clints' thin soil makes them invisible, but the grikes are sometimes apparent and treacherous and stepping into one could be painful. Jim emphasizes that grikes can be big enough to shelter bears and that this region has the second greatest density of caves in Wisconsin. In spring snow meltwater inundates the alvar, but it's usually dry in the summer, except at the bottom of the deepest grikes.

Trees here aren't expansive like that 400-year-old oak on open land but some bur oaks and white oaks here are very old. The area also includes rare plants, like cream gentian, and on the talus slope an old-growth mesic forest. Owned jointly by the DNR and the Northern Wisconsin Land Trust, its 146 acres on either side of Highway 57 are easy to pass without knowing it's there.

Our final stop is Red Banks itself, a small area on cliffs above Green Bay, where a gazebo has another Nicolet marker. Much of the surrounding area is now owned by the Ho-Chunk. For all the attention to Nicolet's landing and the beginning of Wisconsin's European-American history, commemoration of the landscape should acknowledge the peoples who lived here before Nicolet put it on a French map. Establishing the Red Banks Savanna Historic District and Heritage Area would do that.

My sympathy with the desire to commemorate the vanished is likely linked with the obscurity of Escarpment elements here. Having wandered prominent sites, like Oakfield Ledges and High Cliff, I've been surprised by how more hidden sites, like the caves at Ledge View and Cherney Maribel, the alvar, the gorges of Wequiock and Fonferek, affect me. By expanding my sense of the Niagara Cuesta, they remind me that the Niagara Escarpment is something more than a Ledge.

6

If Wisconsin is shaped like a hand palm down, the Door Peninsula, between Green Bay and Lake Michigan, is its bony thumb. Brown County extends as far up as its first knuckle, Fonferek's Glen solidly in its landlocked portion, Wequiock Falls about a mile and a half inland from Green Bay, and Cecil Depeau Bay Shore Park located right on the bay. *Roadside Geology of Wisconsin* reports that Bay Shore Park "exposes about 50 feet of lower Silurian dolomite along a steep road down to a boat landing and a stony beach," and the 360° "Interactive Virtual Tour" on a county website claims its Bay Shore Park Trail, "nestled along the gorgeous Niagara Escarpment for a short distance," will "take you back in time 600 million years." As the virtual tour rotates along a narrow path, I tilt the angle up and down, zoom in closely on a high talus mound and scan upwards to see the high bluff edge. The Niagara Escarpment and Cuesta underlie all of the Door Peninsula and form most of its shorelines, making them a promising place to explore bluffs.

On an overcast May morning I park near Bay Shore's picnic grounds and its playground with a blocky version of a two-masted schooner. A sign urges caution on "a rugged trail through a natural area which presents rugged terrain, steep cliffs, and falling rock." At the Escarpment's lip, I descend narrow, slick, leaf-coated stone steps, noting the layers of dolomite deposits I pass through.

The path winds northeast close to the bluffs, below over-hanging rocks that seem barely supported. The Escarpment rises high, the bluffs uneven, niches and fractures appear often, and water from the morning's rain drips off the rocks. I often lean into niches and crevices. The space between the mass of the cuesta and a semi-separated slice of scarp seems almost precarious, as if that freestanding section might topple any moment. Occasionally, erosion on all sides form pillars, like squat legs holding up a dense armoire. Some deep recesses cut into the bluffs from top to bottom; high up, trees cling to small stone outcroppings. For a view back down the trail, I climb a solid wooden staircase at the trail's south end, surprisingly relieved to get out from under the bluffs. The Escarpment here is exposed and intimidating; I feel exposed and vulnerable at its base.

Midway back along the trail, weathered stone steps lead to a long set of metal stairs descending beyond the bottom of the talus to the park's beach and boat launch area. The exposed bluff rises high up the slope. I trudge up the beach access road cutting through the escarpment, its slant helping me appreciate the Ledge's height here and how much is buried under its own debris. Midway up, where the bluffs are more fully exposed, I'm reminded how much geological strata roadcuts reveal.

On my way back to my car, I think how imposing the bluffs were as I walked below ledges jutting out from them, how I could sense the Ledge's mass and scope.

* * *

The Door Peninsula invites us to confront issues of chang-ing elevation of landmasses and changing lake levels (and identities). We consider landmasses stable, solid, subject to deposition or erosion but not flexible in altitude. But an ice sheet can be so massive and so heavy—the Wisconsin Glaciation was over 1,000 feet thick—that it depresses the land it crosses up to thirty percent of the ice's thickness. The elevation in northern and eastern Wisconsin dropped more than 300 feet. When the ice retreated the land rebounded, over thousands of years, to reach levels prior to glaciation. The ice was thicker over the Door Peninsula than over areas further south and it stayed longer; the rebounding here occurred later.

While that rebounding was happening water levels of what became the Great Lakes also rose and fell and, depending on the ice sheet's location, lake outlets altered as well. Lake Michigan once drained into the Illinois River, until the ice retreated and allowed drainage across the Straits of Mackinac into Lake Huron; at another time the combined waters of Lakes Michigan and Huron drained across Ontario through the Ottawa River directly into the St. Lawrence River. After the ice sheets receded from Wisconsin, Lakes Michigan, Superior, and Huron together formed Glacial Lake Algonquin, then eventually drained to a level where they separated. Due to rebounding, Superior rose enough to drain into Huron and Lake Michigan's water level rose enough to drain again at Chicago, a stage known as the Nipissing phase of Lake Michigan. Eventually all five Great Lakes took on their present shorelines and water levels and pattern of drainage.

On the Door Peninsula evidence of those earlier lake incarnations can be seen on the landscape. In the thousands of years Green Bay and Lake Michigan went through these alterations, they did the same beach building and shaping that they do today, but the lowering and raising of water levels and the rebounding of the land itself altered the elevations at which beaches were formed. At Red Banks Savanna, at the southern end of Green Bay, the Escarpment is distant from the shoreline and a series of terraces step down to the west. Further north on the peninsula are clear indications of the Algonquin and Nipissing levels. At some places the Escarpment precipitously abuts the shoreline, but at others the Escarpment is a series of shelves retreating into the cuesta and those lake levels are markedly present. Because of rebounding, the Lake Algonquin level, dating back to 11,000 BCE, will be higher than the Nipissing level, dating back to 5000 BCE. At almost no time will anyone feel that they are standing on a beach.

* * *

A high wall of Niagara dolostone lines a curve as I cross into Door County. I'd seen it a month ago, when I attended the Ice Age Trail Alliance's annual conference in Sturgeon Bay. Primed by a talk by David Mickelson, lead author of *Geology of the Ice Age National Scenic Trail*, I'd hiked in Potawatomi State Park with other attendees. April was cold, the trails often icy, and our attention was on a stretch of the Ice Age Trail in the park, its eastern terminus a tower overlooking Sturgeon Bay, an arm of Green Bay. Our walks on the Niagara cuesta didn't focus on the Escarpment, but Will Stewart informed me of specific sites I could find in the future. Now in May, spring more advanced and trails hopefully thawed, I return to the park.

I wind my way up to the observation tower at the north end. On the April hike several of us climbed the 75-foot tower to gaze across ice-coated waters at the frozen shorelines of two small islands and a spit of land curving like a claw around Sawyer Harbor. On the eastern shoreline of Sturgeon Bay, we identified Algonquin and Nipissing lake levels in notches in its profile. That winter, over 90 percent of the Great Lakes had frozen over and men walked across the ice from one of the islands. Now boats motor across the waters.

I drive past the tower down to the intersection with Shoreline Road. In April, we clambered over or around mounds of snow blocking the road to the tower. Walking near Mickelson I asked about the low stretch of dolomite cliff face the road cut through and he said the tower stood on the highest level of the escarpment. Later, I noticed Escarpment outcroppings beyond the trees on the landward side of the road. Now, following Will Stewart's advice, I park near the boat launch and walk back up the road. Bluffs here rise as high as the level of the base of the tower, but trees growing out of the talus make it hard to see them, especially driving by. Walking slowly while staying alert to passing traffic, I see caves and ledges with cedars perched upon and around them, a few very close to the road. In places where sky appears through the trees, I gauge how high up the tower looms, atop a 150-foot bluff.

Further south on Shoreline Road, I park again. In April, on the Ice Age Trail, we hiked south from the tower through the woods and veered east toward Shoreline Road in steep descents. A set of rock steps took us from the Algonquin lake level down to the Nipissing lake level, not far from the intersection where we'd started. The Ice Age Trail crossed the road, dropped down another level of Escarpment, and then headed south through tall cedars, between the low dolomite bluffs and the drop-off to the rocky beach. It emerged from the shoreline and ascended through a loop that brought it to a tricky descent over moss-coated dolomite bluffs. The buses were waiting at an open picnic area.

I walk back up Shoreline Road until I see those stairs heading into the woods, then drop off the road down onto the level above the shoreline, turning north as Will advised. The escarpment is exposed in either direction, but more massive dolomite blocks are to the north. One section without support hangs tilted between neighboring sections, as if trying to fall but they wouldn't let it. The blocks have mass and density and occasional uniformity. Cedars grow out of them, and vertical, straight rocks are poised at beach edge. I consider the locations I saw on the inland Ice Age Trail hike and those I've seen today, and feel well acquainted with the Escarpment here, more attuned to the changes in levels, more aware of what lies below the surfaces the talus covers.

7

In late May at Cave Point County Park on the Door
Peninsula's Lake Michigan shoreline, lake waters batter
the slope of the cuesta. The county park is surrounded by
Whitefish Dunes State Park, best known for Old Baldy, at
93 feet above the lake Wisconsin's tallest dune. Cave Point
takes up only 19 acres of Whitefish Dunes' 863 acres, but
it's the principal place to see the effects of shoreline erosion
on the cuesta.

From Cave Point's lot, a short gravel trail to the shoreline points at blue water beyond a tree-lined bluff with a
hint of rock outcropping at the edge. Turning north on a
narrow intersecting trail, I feel the wind from the lake, hear
water thumping against the rocks, and come out of the
trees. The scarp the waves cut into the cuesta is relatively
low, its layers jagged and uneven. The talus is barely sloped
and when waves recede, flat layers of rock appear beneath
shallow waters. On a promontory at the edge of a scallop of
shoreline, an arch has formed where, over time, support for
rocks above may give way. Where the mottled stone shelf
is puddled but high enough for safe walking, a man and
a woman have ventured out to examine the pitted surface
and view the bluffs head on. Elsewhere the lip of stone is
higher, the weathered bluff further back, enough for plant
growth out of the cracks. Deep crevices pierce the bluffs at
various angles.

The shoreline is sometimes deeply scalloped, the lake still carving away at the indentations. I feel the impact of onrushing waves at the base of the bluff I stand on. When bluffs get lower, I take the trail back south, toward higher bluffs. Below them I see ledges under the water and often under one another. At one place, below trees firmly anchored in stone and well above the waterline, a mound of snow still rests in a depression scooped out deeply into the rock, hidden from sun and all but the stormiest waves. It's a reminder that not only wave action but also snow and ice, freeze and thaw, contribute to the wearing away of the rock.

I step onto promontories to scan embayments. Some sea caves are carved deeply into the bluff; many are underwater. At lower lake levels people can enter some on foot, but as Doris Green writes, in *Wisconsin Underground*, "you know the caves are there, hidden beneath your feet. The booming of the waves hurling against their walls drowns out other sounds, their power almost ominous." At several places, I watch waves crash in and withdraw, concealing caves, then exposing them. Green observes, "Cave Point makes geologic change visible; you can clearly see the impact of wind, water, and temperature on this land over many years." Erosion's process is evident here, obvious in large caves, evident in submerged caves when waves roll away. The beating of the waves has dug away at the base of the bluffs, and the flat surfaces beneath the water beyond the shoreline make clear how fallen rocks get leveled. "With the wind in your face and the thundering waves pounding the rock layers beneath your feet," Green writes, "you can feel the dominion of nature in this place."

The cliffs are higher farther south. Rugged, rough rock is exposed on the surface, and trees rising above them on exposed roots barely have a toehold anchoring them. Some cliffs are straight, almost as smooth as quarry walls; at others, a block of stone lies at an angle, propped up against the cliff at one end and resting on a lower shelf just beneath the water. Once underlayers have been worn away, ledges jutting out from the tops of the cliffs inevitably crack off and plunge below. I see several, upper ends mostly smooth and dry, lower ends wet and wave washed. One block has trees rooted in the upper end, where the block had been attached to the cliff. I lose track of the numbers of rock layers in the walls. In some places small rocks have piled up, as if they hoped to form a cobblestone beach; in other places I can't gauge the depth of the waters.

Once in a while, where cliffs are most exposed to the lake, I listen to the lake and the wind, watch the waves roll in and roll away, observe waves and rock working steadily at geologic change.

* * *

I cruise headlands north of Sturgeon Bay, which cut a deep incision into the peninsula from Green Bay. Early travelers portaged from Lake Michigan into Sturgeon Bay to reach Green Bay and the Fox River Valley without risking the potentially turbulent passage at Door's tip. In time a ship canal was excavated between Sturgeon Bay and Lake Michigan, making northern Door County more island than peninsula.

Talking about karst in Wisconsin, Dott and Attig emphasize sinkholes on the Door Peninsula, where, north of Sturgeon Bay, "geologists have mapped hundreds of karst features." The "most pervasive impact of karst," they assert, "may be the pattern of the valleys," all following fractures in dolomite that glacial and river erosion enlarged. A preglacial

drainage pattern extended eastward-flowing rivers in northern Wisconsin into the valley of an Ancient Michigan River,
the precursor of the Lake Michigan lakebed. At various
times draining Glacial Lake Oshkosh, such rivers as the
Manitowoc, West Twin, Kewaunee, and Ahnapee flowed
east down the cuesta's slope. More northerly rivers, preglacial
versions of the Peshtigo and the Menominee, likely flowed
from the west side of what is now Green Bay across what is
now the Door Peninsula. Once Green Bay was formed and
those western rivers emptied into it, their eastern channels
were filled by rising lake levels. One channel became Sturgeon Bay; another became Death's Door Passage, the body
of water dividing the Door Peninsula from Washington
Island. The port where a ferry line connects the peninsula
to Washington Island is roughly forty miles north-northeast of the city of Sturgeon Bay, the county seat. The entire
county, with all its promontories and embayments, has 250
miles of shoreline.

* * *

To travel due north 17 miles from Cave Point County Park
on Lake Michigan to Peninsula State Park perched above
Green Bay, I cross the Niagara Cuesta. From the northern
entrance, I drive to the Eagle Tower, a 76-foot-high structure on the park's highest point, 180-foot-high Eagle Bluff.
I climbed the tower in April, on an Ice Age Trail Alliance
hike, and remember the view—to the east frozen Eagle
Harbor and the distant town of Ephraim, to the north the
distinctive shape of Horseshoe Island, to the west Nicolet Bay and Welker's Point extending north. More islands
pop up west of the park: large Chambers Island, hosting a
lighthouse, and the four privately owned Strawberry Islands,
cutely named Adventure, Jack, Pirate, and Little Strawberry.

Like the Sister Islands, a State Natural Area further north, all these islands are outliers of the Niagara Cuesta. In April they were ice-bound, but now the ice is gone, and every inlet of Green Bay is blue, open, and bright with sunlight. I light out for the two-mile loop below the bluffs called the Eagle Trail, impassable in last month's snow and ice but clear now.

Stone steps lead to an extensive walled rock terrace, constructed from remains of a quarry transformed, when Peninsula State Park opened in 1909, into a picnic site, with a panoramic view of Eagle Harbor and a chance to stroll across dolomite blocks and sit on stone layers. The Escarpment here is neatly trimmed and shorn and the opposite shoreline displays shelves from Algonquin and Nipissing lake levels.

On a slow descent through open woods toward the shoreline, I pass warnings about the trail's difficulty, often coated with last autumn's leaf fall still soaked in last winter's snowfall. Climbing down from the highest level of the park to the lowest, from time to time I'm aware of descending another several layers of escarpment, some of it exposed under leaves and behind trees. At the shoreline I step onto the beach and listen to shallow waves ripple over the rocks and cobbles. The shoreline, solidly lined with tall trees, arches out into Eagle Harbor.

The trail weaves through trees well above the shoreline, from this spot above Eagle Harbor north around the point below Eagle Tower and west toward Nicolet Bay, before climbing back up to where I parked. It's a two-mile-long loop, the lower stretch probably only a mile or so, and rocks, roots, and rubble from eroded escarpment make it sometimes treacherous walking.

Hiking first through cedars with open ground below, then through woods rife with scraggly saplings and thick undergrowth, I can barely see low sections of the Escarpment through shadows, tree limbs, and fallen branches and trunks. Occasionally I discern higher sections, as if the Escarpment here falls in a series of ledges down to the shoreline. Closer to the Escarpment I sometimes see rubble, as if that portion has collapsed altogether, and sometimes see low bluffs thoroughly pierced by tree roots, fractured and discontinuous. The trail veers closer again and cedars are so thick they almost overwhelm the rocks rising above and around deep crevices and niches.

Then the bluffs rise high, no longer a step-like sequence of ledges but a continuous wall. Craning my neck to catch a glimpse of sky makes me appreciate their height. In places crevices have grown into caves. The trail gets much rougher nearing the bluffs. I'm scrambling more often, climbing onto rocks and over fallen trees and sometimes creeping under them and around exposed tree roots. Some cedar roots are large and complicated, twined around one another and anchored not only in rock layers but also beneath rockfall. And then I'm at the base of the bluffs, picking my way across talus, crossing fallen rock rather than a well-groomed trail, peering into crevices and caves close to me. Cave floors are littered with fallen blocks, and pillars eroded into the base seem inadequate to support the mass of stone above them. I move slowly, taking in what I pass of the Escarpment and watching my footing across rocks and tree roots. At times a stretch extends straight up and shows me layer after layer of deposition. The lowest levels are the Mayville Formation, the highest levels the Burnt Bluff Group, and together they display how much was deposited during the nearly thirty million years of the Silurian Period; the Manistique and Engadine Formations once raised the escarpment even higher, before erosion scoured them away. Foliage grows on the talus at the base and on the top, but here the escarpment, largely free of plant growth, gleams in the sunshine.

My slow progress and my tendency to keep looking up as well as crouching and peering within crevices rewards me with a view of a cave entrance high up on the wall. Along the Green Bay shoreline, the Escarpment has many such caves, exposed when lake levels were higher. This one is thirty feet above water level—I've seen photos in geology books. Paull and Paull point out that 180-foot-high Eagle Bluff shows signs of varying lake levels, the Glacial Lake Algonquin level 60 feet above the present shoreline and Glacial Lake Nipissing 21 feet above it. The cave "was cut thousands of years ago by the same processes of wave erosion that are now operating at Cave Point." I try to imagine the sea caves at Cave Point elevated high above me by glacial rebound, as this cave was; if, for a few million years, the lake clawed away at the bluffs those caves formed in, and lake levels were similarly lower, some would be as incongruous as this, so isolated and deep.

I continue slowly along the Escarpment, still noting the crevices and pillars and talus. I could spend a long time investigating this section and thinking about the geologic processes that brought all this into being. After the trail moves away from the Escarpment, I begin an easier, faster climb through the woods than the descent had been, passing exposed sections higher up and climbing a long set of stone steps formed from their layers, to arrive just west of the tower. The Eagle Panorama overlook offers views of offshore islands, the point extending up Nicolet Bay, and, across Green Bay, Upper Michigan. I stand there awhile, aware of the park spreading across the cuesta behind me, remembering the Escarpment below me.

* * *

The Door Peninsula was named for the rough navigational passage between Green Bay and Lake Michigan termed by the French "Porte des Mortes" ("Death's Door"). Before Green Bay's glacial formation, it was a channel emptying into the Ancient Michigan River preceding Lake Michigan. North of Death's Door are Washington Island and a chain of islands crossing the gap between Green Bay and Lake Michigan. The Niagara Escarpment in mainland Wisconsin ends at the Door Peninsula's tip, 200-foot-high cliffs accessible on foot from above or by boat from below, along a narrow, rocky shoreline. The coastline is indented every so often with bays between promontories. Peninsula State Park juts out between Fish Creek Harbor and Eagle Harbor, Ellison Bluff juts out just south of Ellison Bay, and Death's Door Bluff, between Green Bay and Garret Bay, is the westernmost of the northern shoreline bluffs. Along the tip Porte des Mortes Park, Ellison Bluff County Park with Ellison Bluff State Natural Area, and Door Bluff Headlands County Park are good places to view headlands formed by the Escarpment.

I've long been aware of cuesta forests and the trees that grow on the lip of the scarp, out of talus at its base, and even out of niches in dolomite with little soil to sustain plant growth. Trunks rise above thick gnarled roots wedged between rock layers or in cracks and crevices and fractures, as if earth were unnecessary for nourishment or stability, as if they drew their strength from sheer rock itself.

These are eastern white cedars, *Thuja occidentalis*, referred to by Peter E. Kelly and Douglas W. Larson in their subtitle for *The Last Stand* as "the Ancient Cliff-Forest of the Niagara Escarpment," chiefly centered on Ontario but relevant for the entire arc. Of escarpment trees they write: "Roots weave their way along fissures or ledges. They seek out cavities on the face and plunge into networks of small cracks and fissures. Sometimes there is soil; sometimes there is not." They note that, though we think of age in forest trees in terms of size—the General Sherman tree in Sequoia National Park is "a 2,100-year-old giant sequoia that is the largest tree on earth"—circumstances of climate and location may influence size without impacting age. The ages of ancient white cedars, considerably smaller than sequoias, can be astonishing—Kelly counted tree rings in dead cedars found in talus of the Ontario Escarpment and discovered one that died at 1,653 years; another had 1,567 annual rings but an estimate of missing tree rings suggested an age of 1,890 years. The exposure to wind and weather and the tenuous terrain from which they grow keeps them compact and tight, and locations at the escarpment edge or out of the cliff face makes them less susceptible to the lumber-harvesting that cleared so much of North American forests. Ancient trees are found where there has been relatively little agriculture and sparse populations. Scientists discovered "the world's oldest red cedar at the bluff north of Greenleaf in Brown County," estimated at over 1,200 years old; a 507-year-old white cedar was discovered on Sven's Bluff in Peninsula State Park and a 616-year-old white cedar was located near Fish Creek, south of the park.

Coming to the Door County headlands, I'm as much aware of the cedars on the Escarpment's edge as of the cliff face that falls below them.

* * *

On a warm mid-May day, I drive with windows open into Ellison Bluff County Park. Bugs and butterflies flitter about and a profusion of trilliums brighten the sparsely green floor of a forest of birch, aspen, maple, ash, beech, and oak. Overhead a clear blue sky; to the west low white cumulus clouds are placidly suspended above a haze blurring Green Bay's opposite shore. At the Scenic Overlook, a long series of wooden steps lead to a deck facing the bay. A separate, narrower overlook with metal fencing hangs out over the bluff, allowing a view along the Escarpment. The cliff face is light grey, sheer, and nearly two hundred feet high. Cedars grow out of niches and hang off ledges. With binoculars I survey a thick twisted trunk out of which grow punier limbs hanging down and an auxiliary trunk rising up the cliff face. One white cedar here was determined to be 250 years old. I suspect it took a very long time for this cedar to extend as far as it has.

Beyond the straight, tall trees at the Escarpment bottom, dolostone cobbles lay in bright shades of green in a narrow band close to the shoreline, as if carefully spaced to form a level surface. Further out the green is darker and the shoreline seems to drop away, and then the whole of the bay is blue. A white-crowned sparrow pecks at the dirt in a clear space near the cliff top fence while I listen to the breeze, watch clouds above the bay, and appreciate his company.

On the gravel road to Door Bluff Headlands County Park the sun shining through a canopy-less birch, oak, and spruce forest is soaked up by abundant trilliums. The road ends in a turnaround with no sign of a scenic overlook, but a worn footpath, not clearly marked, leads off down a rocky slope. The angle of descent makes me wonder how far it will be to the edge of the Escarpment. The trail shifts west into a cedar forest, the trees large and close together, the canopy shading a forest floor with scant undergrowth. At the unfenced edge of the escarpment, I'm aware of how much cedar grows on the cuesta, how much out of the cliff face, how much in the talus below. The cuesta slopes toward the lip of the bluffs and the thin soil on top makes me walk carefully over thick half-exposed roots. It's impossible to tell the depth of the root system but the tangle often looks like a nest of snakes. Roots of one tree stretch across roots of other trees, and there is almost no clear ground among the trees. I step gingerly through the cedars and stop often to look up from my footing, so that I don't see only roots as I wander.

Nearing the cliff edge, I make sure there's a tree between open air and me. Cedars hang off the very edge. Occasionally a ledge or shelf seems to be a single layer of dolomite without support, but a good-sized cedar still grows on top of it, seemingly with no place for its roots to anchor. In some places a limb will grow horizontally out toward the

 bay, then shoot up vertically in a bicep curl; in other places the base of the tree will be on a lower ledge and its roots will seem to have climbed back up to firmer ground on the bluff. Sometimes I get a clear view of the lake edge, that bright green strand of submerged cobbles and slabs. The stones clearly lie on a flat ledge still sticking out into the bay to where the Escarpment itself once stood.

Since I entered the cedars, I've lost track of any discernible path, but turning back to follow the lip of the ledge, eventually a path becomes clear. I am alone in the park. Stepping away from the headlands, I'm aware of having come as far as I can on the Door Peninsula, how far I've followed the Niagara Escarpment in Wisconsin. That feeling of accomplishment is accompanied by something more, the realization of how much I now sense the escarpment beneath my feet wherever I go. That thought makes me tread more slowly, more deliberately, through the trees.

Boundary Waters
Part One

I had compartmentalized my travels along the arc of the Escarpment among political entities: three states, one province, two countries, governmental boundaries organizing both mental journey and physical wandering. But the Escarpment's geological flow on scientific maps points to continuous underground connections, a trail of dolomitic breadcrumbs. A conflict surfaces at the islands lining up between Wisconsin's Door Peninsula and Michigan's Garden Peninsula.

On land the border between the states runs from Lake Superior's south shore, midway between Michigan's Keweenaw Peninsula and Wisconsin's Bayfield Peninsula, southeast to the mouth of the Menominee River between Marinette, Wisconsin and Menominee, Michigan, east across Green Bay, through the Rock Island Passage, and down the middle of Lake Michigan. Supposedly, the Niagara Escarpment in Wisconsin ends at Rock Island, begins in Michigan with St. Martin's, the next island north, then arcs east across the Upper Peninsula to Drummond Island, at the border between Michigan and Ontario in the middle of the St. Mary's River. Those are clear governmental boundaries.

Political boundaries seldom conform to geological boundaries. The islands between the Door and Garden Peninsulas are geologically linked, as are large and small islands at the mouth of the St. Mary's River and Lake

Huron's northern shoreline. Both chains have in common the Niagara Escarpment, its arc running through the Upper Peninsula's southern portion.

In Wisconsin, Washington Island and Rock Island seem like distinct entities, accessible by separate ferry rides, concluding moments of a particular journey. But learning that other islands range beyond the state boundary in Death's Door Passage led me to see them as a geological unit, an essential, if multi-segmented, part of the Niagara Escarpment.

In a 1940 article, Robert R. Shrock traces the Escarpment through soundings on a U.S. War Department navigational chart. It is interrupted at Death's Door Passage, continues along the western side of Plum Island and the western shore of Washington Island to Boyer Bluff, follows the north shore almost to Rock Island, continues along the western shore of Rock Island to Pottawatomie Point, is interrupted by the Rock Island Passage, and surfaces again at St. Martin Island in Michigan. The interruptions are subaqueous valleys parallel to Sturgeon Bay leading into Lake Michigan. Shrock observes: "If the waters of Green Bay and Lake Michigan were lowered 200 feet, the archipelago across the entrance to the bay would then appear as a rather narrow, serrated ridge with a precipitous cliff—the Niagara Escarpment—along the west side and a rather steep, eastward slope along the opposite side." I appreciate that image of the Escarpment as an exposed land bridge between Wisconsin and Michigan, since the arc of the Escarpment isn't all that apparent on any regular maps.

The chain runs southwest to northeast across the passage between Green Bay and Lake Michigan. Calling up different islands on an Internet satellite map, I view green beads of varying sizes sprawling across a blue cloth. They are generally known as the Grand Traverse Islands, a moniker bestowed by French-Canadian voyageurs. If you think of "traversing" that passage between Green Bay and Lake Michigan, or in terms of geological bodies rather than state boundaries, it seems an appropriate name. The islands are also identified or cataloged in other ways: the Green Bay National Wildlife Refuge, a native bird preserve established in 1912; the 1913 Gravel Island National Wildlife Refuge containing two inaccessible islands; the 29 acre Wisconsin Islands Wilderness Area protecting nesting grounds for herring gulls, ring-billed gulls, and double-crested cormorants; and a U.S. Fish and Wildlife Service (USFWS) management complex that includes four refuges and a wetland district in Wisconsin.

In 2014, to further protect the Niagara Escarpment and preserve maritime history, the Friends of the Grand Traverse Islands promoted The Grand Traverse Islands National Lakeshore Proposal, which would include up to 16 islands: Pilot, Plum, Detroit, Rock, St. Martin, Poverty, Summer, Little Summer, Spider, Gravel, Hog, Fish, Gull, Little Gull, Gravelly, and Rocky. It calls the Escarpment "one of the greatest defining geological features of North America" and "one of the world's unique natural wonders" and argues for support of "regional efforts to earn a UNESCO Global GeoPark designation for the Escarpment in both the United States and Canada."

The proposal helps alter my perspective on the boundary waters between Wisconsin and Michigan.

8

Light fog hangs above the twisting road to Northport, at the tip of the Door, and looking toward the harbor from the Washington Island Ferry dock this May morning, I can barely see beyond the breakwall. More than a dozen others trickle in for the Ledge Tour, including Sherrill Andersen from the Lakeshore Natural Resources Partnership and Eric Fowle from the Niagara Escarpment Resource Network, expecting to carpool around Washington Island.

We sail into thick fog above Death's Door Passage, the waters calm this morning. Lake flies or midges flit around us at the dock, almost coating the seats on the ferry's open top deck. The blast of the ferry's foghorn occasionally drives us into the cabin below.

Except for cormorants and gulls floating near the vessel, we mostly view fog as we cross. At Plum Island, a low patch of land with a small lighthouse and scruffy foliage, the fog rises momentarily and closes in quickly. A ferry from the island churns by like a ghost ship. We see nothing of Pilot Island, where, we're told, cormorant guano has destroyed the vegetation. I'm uncertain whether to regret not viewing it.

About forty minutes later, the fog lifts near Washington Island. Beyond Detroit Island, a long, low island on Washington' southwest corner—in lower water levels it would be a peninsula—swans glide near the shoreline. The ferry docks in Detroit Harbor and Sandy Petersen, our tour leader, leads us into the Welcome Center where the ferry owner, Dick Purinton, stands before a large map with contours of the lake bottom to tell us something about where we are.

Dick points out islands beyond Washington Island, including Rock Island and islands in Michigan waters leading to the Garden Peninsula, which he terms the mirror image of the Door. Emphasizing the region's historic remoteness, he mentions how people from the island and the tip of the Door went more readily north to Escanaba, in Michigan, than to Sturgeon Bay or Green Bay. Eric grouses amiably that the Upper Peninsula should belong to Wisconsin, to which it is attached, rather than to Michigan. I don't mention my sympathies with those in the Upper Peninsula who want it to be a separate state, called Superior.

We caravan to the Stavkirke (Stave Church), which imitates a historical church in Borglund, Norway, to emphasize the island's Nordic heritage. We rush up its prayer path without contemplation and admire the church's splendid design, the interior solid and small, a model ship hanging in the center, an icon on the wall. Here, as throughout the island, trillium and white and yellow daffodils flourish in the woods, a colorful backdrop to the wooden church.

The Little Lake State Natural Area, owned by the Door County Land Trust, is midway up a peninsula in the island's northwest corner, jutting between Green Bay and Washington Harbor. Access is usually on a wooded trail, but for the tour we park on the south side, near the Jacobsen Museum, a 1930 log cabin with natural and historical artifacts collected by a Danish immigrant to the island. The Thorstein Veblen Study Cabin stands nearby, unrestored and filled with materials to refurbish it.

Terrie Cooper, Land Program Director of the Door County Land Trust, leads us into the natural area past private homes and through a cedar forest between Green Bay and Little Lake. During the Lake Nipissing period, wave action sweeping cobbles down the western shore of the island closed a bay and formed Little Lake. When waters receded, the lake was cut off. Fishermen cutting a channel between Green Bay and Little Lake luckily realized in time that, because Little Lake was three feet higher than Green Bay, their channel, if completed, would empty the lake. The depression left behind is a marked channel of exposed cobblestones that hints at what's everywhere below the surface.

On the beach we look north for the high dolomite cliffs of Boyer Bluff, but the fog obscures them. The rocky beach doesn't promise easy or quick passage to the cliffs for a closer look. Some of us examine the dolomite cobblestones for fossil remains of corals while Terrie Cooper shows others where Thorstein Veblen's cabin once stood. The economist, who explained "conspicuous consumption" in *The Theory of the Leisure Class*, came to the island to learn Icelandic from immigrants who settled there. He established a summer retreat here in 1915. When the Land Trust realized the cabin was on their newly acquired natural area, islanders contributed to the expense of moving it near the Jacobsen Museum.

We lunch above the bay at nearby Peoples Park and gaze down at the cobblestone beach and a stretch of clear bedrock beneath green water. Its flatness and fracture lines resemble a submerged paved area, like those at Ellison Bluff and Door Bluff on the Door.

At Schoolhouse Beach Park, the beach curves around the bottom of Washington Harbor, a wide-open sweep of dolomitic cobblestones extending toward Boyer Bluff, stretching green in the distance above blue water. Most of the shoreline here is privately owned, residences visible through the trees. We stroll the beach, examining the small, smooth, wave-rounded stones.

The tour takes us inland to Mountain Park where a steep set of stairs leads up to a wooden tower. While some people check out rock formations at the mountain's base, I join others heading for the tower, taking the stairs two at a time to the top of the bluff, then clambering up the tower for an overview of the island. In the distance to the north, through binoculars, I see Rock Island's bare, sheer coastal cliffs. Beyond it I also see St. Martin's Island where the arc of the escarpment reaches into Michigan.

At Jackson Harbor in the northeast corner, we get a closer view of Rock Island, its shoreline cliffs showing us what we might have seen at Boyer Bluff. On the way back to Detroit Harbor to catch the ferry, my efforts to remember the Washington Island tour compete with burgeoning plans to reach Rock Island, the end of the Wisconsin Escarpment.

* * *

The stratigraphy of the Niagara Escarpment includes layers of dolomite deposited over millennia throughout the Silurian Period. The earliest, lowest layer and, according to Luczaj, "the principal cliff-forming unit" in Wisconsin, is termed the Mayville Formation, visible at High Cliff State Park, Ledge County Park, Oakfield Ledge State Natural Area, Fonferek and Wequiock Falls, Ledge View Nature Center, Cherney Maribel Caves County Park, and Bayshore County Park. It is anywhere from 66 feet thick in Fond du Lac County to 270 feet thick in Door County.

The Mayville Formation was succeeded by the Burnt Bluff Group, consisting of two distinctive forms, the lower Byron Formation and, above it, the Hendricks Formation. "Because of its thickness and resistance to erosion," Luczaj tells us, it is "a prominent cliff-forming unit, especially along the western shore of the Door Peninsula north of Little Sturgeon Bay." Cliffs range between 100 and 200 feet high, the most prominent at Potawatomi State Park, Peninsula State Park, Ellison Bay Bluff County Park, Door Bluff County Park, Boyer Bluff on Washington Island, and Pottawatomie Point on Rock Island.

The next Silurian layer, the Manistique Formation, is distinguished by abundant fossils and more easily eroded than the Burnt Bluff. The Engadine Formation is the topmost and thinnest layer, only thirty to forty feet thick. Due to multiple glaciations and long periods of erosion, the Manistique and Engadine Formations have little prominence in northeastern Wisconsin. Geologists often fine-tune distinctions among lithologies (types of rocks), but in my wandering, I'm unlikely to distinguish accurately among those four types, though I keep in mind that sites south of Door County and Brown County display primarily Mayville dolomite and sites from Brown County north through Door County display Burnt Bluff dolomite.

Shrock's thorough and detailed study of Washington Island's geology describes it as "essentially a large, differentially sculptured block of dolomite tipped gently to the southeast so that the individual beds or layers in the block [. . .] descend in a general southeasterly direction at the rate of about 30-40 feet per mile." Its "most conspicuous topographic feature" are the western shoreline cliffs, which start out in the southwest corner "as a low, cobble-covered bluff about 15-20 feet high" and "culminate in the bold face of Boyer Bluff at the northwestern extremity." The Mountain is "a high, rounded, double ridge," made up of "two high, rounded cliffs to the north and a long and broad, gently descending, irregular backslope to the southeast." An illustration shows "The Mountain" to be topped with the Engadine (or in his day, Racine) Formation while Boyer Bluff displays the lower portion of the Manistique above an expanse of the Burnt Bluff. The bluff rises 140 feet above Green Bay, the Mountain 160 feet.

The cobblestones making up the beach on the island's western side are chiefly dolomitic, as is the bluff, but igneous and metamorphic rocks give evidence of the glacier's tendency to carry erratics some distance from their origin. Schrock's Boyer Bluff illustration indicates changing lake levels and shifts in shelves where once were ancient beaches. The bluff face is relatively sheer for the first 70 feet above Green Bay. At around 25 feet a cave carved out by waves is exposed at about the Glacial Lake Nipissing level. At 70 feet a cobble-covered shelf indicates a former beach at the base of a talus-covered slope extending up 30 feet to the Glacial Lake Algonquin level. A jagged bluff rising another 40 feet above that level is topped with glacial drift. The diagram resembles landscape profiles of Potawatomi and Peninsula Parks. Shrock claims that "rocky platforms and cobble ridges, in all essential characters exactly like the ancient ones, may be seen in the process of formation at many points along the present western shore of Washington Island." Geologic forces are at work in the present as they were in the distant past.

Referring to the way the broad backslope of the Cuesta crosses the island to Lake Michigan, Shrock asserts, "One could walk on the same kind of dolomite, with occasional interruptions because of soil, gravel, or vegetation, from the peak of 'The Mountain' to the southeastern tip." Someone tracing that surface "would descend about 160 feet in 8 miles, or at the rate of 20 feet per mile." He makes us aware that we are fully in the presence of the Niagara Escarpment everywhere across Washington Island.

* * *

From the Karfi, the little passenger ferry that takes hikers, campers, and tourists from the northeastern tip of Washington Island to the southwestern tip of Rock Island, the cliffs of the Escarpment gleam white along the shoreline on either island. We follow Rock Island's coast north to Pottawatomie Point, where the lighthouse still stands, invisible behind the forest; crossing back we will see the same kind of coastline at Boyer's Bluff. Both islands each have only one naturally sandy beach, on the south shore. The crossing usually takes only fifteen minutes but ours in August is slowed by windswept waves and stretches into nearly twenty-five.

The ferry ties up below Viking Hall Boat House, a high square hall with tall windows on three sides and a portico surrounding it, above openings allowing boats to moor inside. The stone of the structure is dolomite quarried on the island. The building was commissioned by Chester Thordarson, an Icelandic immigrant who pioneered in high voltage electrical equipment. Having purchased 775 acres of the 915-acre island in 1910, he set aside 745 acres for preservation and constructed outbuildings on only 30 acres behind the boat house.

Viking Hall is modeled on Iceland's Parliament building in Reykjavik, its interior reminiscent of Nordic sagas, with a horned chandelier, enormous fireplace, and wooden furniture engraved with runes and images from Norse legend. An avid rare book collector, Thordarson housed his 11,000-volume library here. On his death in 1945, it became the basis of the University of Wisconsin's rare book collection. After Rock Island became a state park, most of Thordarson's structures were removed, except for a small building now housing Park Headquarters, a stone water tower near the beach, a large wooden gate in Japanese design that once fronted an Oriental-styled garden, and Viking Hall.

Thordarson didn't own the area around Wisconsin's oldest lighthouse on Pottawatomie Point, first built in 1836. Rock Island Passage was a safer route between mainland Wisconsin and upper Michigan than the Portes des Mortes further south. Rebuilt in 1858, the lighthouse was tended by a keeper until 1946, when it became battery-operated; a metal automated tower later replaced it altogether. The Friends of Rock Island, a service group, restored the historic lighthouse and maintain it from Memorial Day to Columbus Day by means of volunteer docents willing to live without electricity or running water for a week or two.

The Thordarson Trail heads mostly uphill on the west side of the island to the lighthouse, a gradual climb after a steeper one just past park ranger's lodgings. We pass around through the high, ornate Japanese gate rough-hewn from island wood. A thick forest of maples, birches, and beeches shades the trail. Cedars grow on the lip of the cliffs, but the open blue of the lake is only a distant light through the trees.

The tour we take guides us up to the lantern room, a replacement of the one the Coast Guard dismantled years before. A replica of a fourth-order Fresnel light, which allowed a wide beam dispersal, was installed to give the building a more historic flavor. To the southwest we see nearby Washington Island and to the north, Michigan's St. Martin's Island and the pale blue outline of the Garden Peninsula. The surrounding waters are a vibrant blue, the islands a lush dark green. We briefly consider applying for the docent job.

A rough trail from the lighthouse to the cliff ends at a long staircase leading down 150 feet to the cobblestone beach. It passes an ancient sea cave left high and dry by the rebounding of the land and lowering of lake levels. The Escarpment above and below the surface together is around 300 feet thick. The stairs take us halfway down.

The escarpment descends in narrow tiers in sheer drops. Shrock and Harvard's 1934 "Composite Profile and Geologic Section at Pottawatomie Point, Rock Island" shows a cobbled ledge at 21 feet as the Glacial Lake Nipissing level, other ledges at 57 feet and 72 feet, and a dolomite talus slope covering Glacial Lake Algonquin levels. Talus then concealed that sea cave. Their diagram shows a quarry at the topmost level, over 150 feet, and all levels are made up of the Burnt Bluff Formation.

After stumbling a little way in either direction along the beach, we climb slowly up the Escarpment and set off on the Thordarson Trail to circle the island back to the Boathouse. Shrock had noted glacial erratics on the highest ridge and found silicified corals in the highest level of the Manistique Formation. The highest elevation on the island is around 793 feet, roughly 200 feet above Lake Michigan. Our elevation around the coastline stays between 600 and 650 feet until midway down the east side, where a gradual descent leads us past an ornate cobblestone water tower and then to the open space where a rustic fishing village once stood. Only a few crumbled foundations remain. The bluffs have gotten lower and lower, and more than halfway across the south shore they disappear altogether.

Near the campground on the spit of land in the island's southwest corner we don swimwear and cross hot, sandy dunes to dip in a chilly lake. Then we walk along the beach, pestered by biting flies but enjoying the breeze and the sense that somehow we've surfaced on a different island than we started out on. On the way back to the Boat House to await the ferry, we pass campers lugging coolers, backpacks, and tents as they disembark from the Karfi. I somewhat envy the people in the Rock Island campsites who have another day to wander the last Wisconsin outpost of the Niagara Escarpment.

*   *   *

Looking back on my travels along the arc of the Escarpment from Brady's Rocks to Rock Island, I'm torn between a sense of accomplishment and a sense of incompleteness. That is, I've been where the Niagara Escarpment is evident in Wisconsin—seen outcroppings barely emergent from underground, leapt crevices and fractures where sections have broken away, stepped to the edges of precipices to see what's below them, to the foot of precipices to see how high they rise, strolled above and slithered below the cuesta, investigated inland and shoreline caves and notches and plunge pools of waterfalls, sailed to outlier islands—and when I rehearse each excursion in my mind, it seems complete in itself, as if each location stood alone, discontinuous from the others.

But that's not physically the case. The outcroppings, the bluffs and the cliffs are the Escarpment's outward show; the cuesta it fronts connects it all. Even in those empty spaces that separate outliers from the cuesta, linkage is deeply buried, as the caves have shown me. I've grown alert to unexpected places where evidence of the Escarpment might turn up. Just as I've come to sense the till and outwash of the Wisconsin glaciation underlying my travels in the eastern part of the state, become alert to glacial formations we've built upon in all my daily living in Waukesha County, so my pursuit of the Escarpment has made me aware of the cuesta that glacial debris covers and sometimes fills. I feel my connections here striving to reach bedrock, in ways almost beyond imagination, in ways intangible and yet somehow deeply felt.

If this is what I've gained from having come a quarter of the way along the arc of the Escarpment, what will I have gained when I've completed it?

9

There's something about a ferry boat, early morning, tied up at Gills Rock in the sun, in the sparkling summer water, the day made for those of us partly made up of islands. The need to cross the water and feel the isolation of the land. The need to come back. To be always comforted, though, with the presence of islands in one's midst.

—Norbert Blei, *Door Steps*

To learn about the island chain between the Door Peninsula and the Upper Peninsula, I read a weblog by the affable kayaker "rotorhead85." He paddled from Gladstone, Michigan across Little Bay de Noc and around the Stonington Peninsula, across Big Bay de Noc to Fayette on the Garden Peninsula, past Little Summer Island (where "Keep Out" signs deterred landing), and camped on (Big) Summer Island farther south. The next day he stopped on Poverty Island, where a storm had once stranded him for two nights, passed up a night on St. Martin Island (more warning signs), paused on Rock Island, and made it to Jackson Harbor on Washington Island. A month later he paddled from Washington Island past Detroit Island and Plum Island and across Death's Door Passage to Gills Rock on the Door Peninsula. His blog demonstrates the possibility of touching all these islands in a kayak.

Hoping to at least view those islands more closely, we sign up for a six-hour cruise sponsored by the Door County Maritime Museum during their mid-June lighthouse festival. The passenger ferry we board at Gills Rock is likely the one Norbert Blei celebrated in *Door Steps* that took him to Washington Island. Blei was Door County's persistent chronicler and celebrant, his books a significant resource into Peninsula life. Perhaps a hundred other passengers board with us. Captain Charley announces that Professor Steven Karges of University of Wisconsin-Janesville, author of *Keepers of the Lights*, about Door County lighthouses, will lead the tour. Most passengers likely came for lighthouses, not for islands.

The vessel backs out of its slip. In Hedgehog Harbor, between Death's Door Bluff to the west and Table Bluff jutting north, we pass low, sheer escarpment shorelines, trees lining bluff tops with cottages and houses perched upon them, steep metal staircases leading to the water's edge. Not so high as at Death's Door Headlands, the bluffs are just as precipitous. Centuries of pounding Green Bay waves have excavated small sea caves low in the bluffs, reminders of the Escarpment.

Today Death's Door Passage is placid, belying its name and shipwreck history. To the east, on the horizon, the scrawny outline of Pilot Island and its abandoned lighthouse look isolated and vulnerable.

The ferry cruises the west side of Washington Island. From time to time the escarpment rises on the shoreline, sea caves and niches above rubbly, narrow beaches. In place of a substantial staircase to the beach, one shoreline home has a very tall ladder propped against the bluff, requiring a hand over hand descent and, worse, ascent. Near the island's northwest corner, I glimpse the patch of cobblestone beach leading inland to Little Lake and gaze at the imposing stretch of Boyer Bluff, exposed escarpment punctuated by sea caves at various levels and laden with thick forest on the cuesta. Rounding Boyer Bluff and passing School-house Beach, Rock Island comes into view toward the east, St. Martin Island ahead to the north.

An hour later, well into the Rock Island Passage, we cross the boundary between Wisconsin and Michigan. Sailing west across Green Bay we would land in Michigan; to reach the mainland border, we would go southwest to the mouth of the Menominee River.

Near St. Martin Island, a shoal extends a mile into the Rock Island Passage, prompting a lighthouse to be constructed in 1905 to protect navigation. A Milwaukee industrialist who owned 1,244 acres, or 94% of the island, intended to build a resort there but left it undeveloped. In 2013, the Nature Conservancy bought his heirs' holdings and the next year 36 acres from another landowner. Most of the island is now Conservancy property and may be transferred to the USFWS for inclusion in the Green Bay National Wildlife Refuge. Over 100 migratory bird species have been documented on the island, along with migrating butterflies, dragonflies, and bats. The Nature Conservancy acknowledges the island to be part of the Niagara

Escarpment and have rare snails and plants associated with significant bluffs. It also supports a diversity of habitats including forest, wetlands and cobblestone beach. When the Conservancy transfers St. Martin Island, it will also donate Rocky Island, a 10-acre island acquired in 1986.

An aerial view in a video on the Conservancy's website shows a lush green landscape, densely forested, surrounded by shoals. Shoreline cliffs seem identical to those of Boyer Bluff on Washington Island and the Door Bluff Headlands. The view gives no sign of anyone ever inhabiting the island.

Clenching binoculars in cold hands, I scan St. Martin. Its topography conforms to the slope of the cuesta, low to the southeast, high to the northwest. The low scarp has sea caves. Nearer the island I can distinguish the Garden Peninsula and other islands further north. The lighthouse here, on the northeast corner, is a six-sided exoskeleton, first activated in 1905 to mark the St. Martin Passage between St. Martin Island and the Gull Islands (Gravelly, Little Gull, and Gull). As we circle slowly offshore and Professor Karges talks about the island's sale to the Nature Conservancy, lighthouse enthusiasts crowd the railings to photograph the metal tower and the boarded-up brick building beside it. Bugs hurry out from the shoreline to greet us and throughout his talk we wave them away from our faces and brush them off our clothing.

Back in open water we head for Poverty Island, another proposed for the Grand Traverse Islands National Lakeshore, and begin to sense the archipelago. The chain is made up not only of St. Martin, Poverty, Gull, Summer and Little Summer islands, but also of scruffy little islets, barely visible above water, largely lifeless, studded with small dead trees, populated with cormorants and gulls. Occasionally we see a solitary white pelican. Between Gull Island to the south and Gravelly Island to the north on our way to Poverty, the scruffy bits of exposed land are likely a site named Gravelly Shoals. When you term locations Gravel, Gravelly, Gull, and Rocky, you've largely stopped identifying unique features.

Poverty Island, between St. Martin and Summer, is small but depths of over 70 feet off its south shore made the northernmost shipping passage for freighters heading east from Escanaba and the iron mines. To warn ships of reefs a brick lighthouse was proposed in 1867, completed in 1875, and eventually the light automated, abandoned, and deactivated. Wildlife has more or less taken over the buildings and the lighthouse's decay has been lamented by lighthouse tourists. We hover offshore, gazing at the defunct and crumbling building, steadily deteriorating. Karges tells us that two years ago the lake was so low that the reefs the lighthouse warned about were easy to see and approach was difficult. The island's insects approach us easily, very many departing with us.

We'll go no further into Michigan waters, leaving Summer Island and Little Summer Island unvisited, close to the Garden Peninsula. Neither island is accessible to the general public, and both contain considerable private holdings. The Michigan Department of Natural Resources owns 1,377 acres there. In the northwest corner of Summer

Island, actual location restricted, archaeologists have excavated a site occupied by various groups of Native Americans
over more than a thousand years, until past the period when
they were in contact with French traders. Later villages were
established by fishermen and loggers and later abandoned.

I'm disappointed not to have at least circled those islands
but satisfied by gaining a sense of the island hopping the
Escarpment does between Wisconsin and Michigan. Aban-
doning the exposed top deck and its cold breeze, we crowd
into the cabin. Feeling comes back slowly into my hands.
Gnats that rushed out from the islands die off, are blown
away, or are swatted and squashed onto our clothing.

The return into Wisconsin waters allows a clear, often
close-up view of Rock Island's northern shoreline and the
bluffs below Pottawatomie Point, a chance to inspect the
Escarpment dead on. Below the lighthouse the trees are
densely packed, the trunks of cedars broad and thick, but
near the turn south along the western coastline, the treeline
rises, the cliffs are dauntingly high and sheer. The base along
the narrow cobblestone beach is fractured and indented with
small caves and niches. The cliff face is deceptively clear.

At noon, when we dock on Rock Island, the spryest
among us launch themselves off for the uphill walk to
the Pottawatomie Point Lighthouse. Sue and I follow less
energetically, skirt the historic building, and climb down to
the beach. I remind myself how narrow that beach is, how
uneven the base of the bluff, how stubbornly the cedars
cling to the rock.

As we retrace our voyage along the west coast of Washington Island, I return to the top deck, lean against the port
railing, and scan Boyer Bluff again. The sea caves are so
square or rectangular they appear to be manmade, though

they clearly derive from the Silurian strata block structure. I realize how challenging the walk to the tip of Boyer Bluff would have been on that narrow rocky beach.

We head into Death's Door and coast Plum Island, a small, low, well-forested island where a lighthouse was. Professor Karges tells us about the use of the lighthouse—established in 1848—as a range light. A large red and white striped steel rectangle is mounted on one side of the light tower; farther down the shoreline another rectangle has been erected. The woods between the two rectangles have been cleared, so that the rectangle on the tower is visible behind the rectangle on the shoreline. An approaching ship can line up the two range lights to assure its crew they are 300 degrees on the compass and adjust their bearings accordingly. We cruise the shoreline until we can line up the rectangles.

Our final stop is Pilot Island, less than two miles southeast of Plum Island, its lighthouse built in 1858 to supplant the Plum Island Light. It is a much smaller island, stark on the distant horizon and even starker the nearer we get to it. Cormorant guano has killed all the vegetation, buildings are in ruins, the highest point is 11 feet above lake level, and drawing close, we see a mass of black cormorants mingling with smaller numbers of white gulls. Black cormorants in bare trees look like ominous menorahs or Gustave Doré illustrations. High reefs keep us considerably offshore. Karges says that in high waves lake water gushes across the island. Pilot Island seems a grim end to the lecture tour for lighthouse people.

Returning to Gills Rock, I study the undulations of bluffs and bays along the peninsula's northern shore. I remember walking bluffs above Death's Door Passage at Door Bluff

Headlands Park and above Green Bay at Ellison Bluff; I consider the islands we've been coasting and islands we've seen in the distance today and in the past. I think how the Niagara Escarpment hopscotches across the Grand Traverse Islands to extend its arc between Wisconsin and Michigan. I try to imagine Death's Door Passage, Rock Island Passage, St. Martin Passage, and Poverty Island Passage gone, dried up, the land links among the islands visible, even walkable, the islands now hills or low mountains. I wonder if I'll ever be able to think of the Door Peninsula of Wisconsin and the Garden Peninsula of Michigan as disconnected from one another anymore.

Michigan

Michigan's state motto is "*Si Quaeris Peninsulam Amoenam Circumspice*"—"If you seek a pleasant peninsula, look about you." Its Lower Peninsula, surrounded by Lakes Michigan, Huron, and Erie, includes the Leelanau Peninsula in the northwest corner, the Old Mission Peninsula dividing Grand Traverse Bay, and the Thumb Peninsula between Lake Huron and Saginaw Bay. The Straits of Mackinac separate the Lower Peninsula from the Upper Peninsula, which stretches between Lakes Michigan and Huron to the south, Lake Superior to the north, and St. Mary's River to the east. The U.P. has peninsulas of its own: the Stonington between Little Bay de Noc and Big Bay de Noc, north of Green Bay; the Garden between Big Bay de Noc and Lake Michigan, directly north of the Door; the St. Ignace at the Straits; the Keweenaw jutting out into Lake Superior; and smaller peninsulas as well.

For nearly thirty years, I taught at Central Michigan University, near "the middle of the mitten," the Lower Peninsula's geographical center. My wife, a Michigan native, and I crossed the Straits of Mackinac on our honeymoon, spent the first night in St. Ignace, and wandered Mackinac Island. In later years we passed through the Upper Peninsula bound for Isle Royale National Park, accessible from the Keweenaw Peninsula. The forests and parks of the Upper Peninsula made it a wilder, less developed place than almost any part of the Lower Peninsula. In no such excursion was I aware that, once off the Mackinac Bridge, I was driving across the Niagara Cuesta and descending the Niagara Escarpment to reach Lake Superior.

The arc of the Escarpment forms the northern boundary of the Michigan Basin, occupied by Lake Michigan, the Straits of Mackinac, Lake Huron, and the whole of the Lower Peninsula. The Silurian strata that forms the Escarpment encircles the southern ends of the state and those lakes, but is nowhere as visible there as in Wisconsin and Ontario. Evidence of the Escarpment can be found along a relatively narrow, roughly 200-mile-long geological corridor in the UP's southern portion. Once the cuesta dips below the northern shoreline of Lakes Michigan and Huron, the further you go into the center of the Lower Peninsula, the deeper the Silurian strata is buried under successive depositions of Devonian and Carboniferous strata and the younger the strata nearer the surface. If, however, you head north, you go further back in time, across the Silurian layers, then Ordovician layers and, along the northern shoreline of the Upper Peninsula, Cambrian layers. Heading west you encounter midway Precambrian bedrock, which makes up the Keweenaw Peninsula and, fifty miles across Lake Superior, Isle Royale. In other words, when my wife and I drove from the center of the Lower Peninsula through the Upper Peninsula to the tip of the Keweenaw Peninsula, we crossed a landscape undergirded by strata ranging from 300 million to 635 million years old. No strata of more recent eras of the Phanerozoic Eon (from 300 MYA to under a million years ago) exists in the Great Lakes region.

Each state or province along the Niagara Escarpment recognizes the special qualities of the terrain. The Michigan

Department of Natural Resources maintains that, in Michigan, "the Niagara Escarpment supports unusual natural communities (such as northern fens in low-lying areas; alvars on flat, droughty areas; and old growth northern white cedar forests on bluffs), as well as rare species (such as the federally Endangered Hines Emerald dragonfly [*Somatochlora hineana*]), and is an important source of cedar for posts, poles, and other uses." Along the arc's Upper Peninsula portion, attention has been paid to Silurian formations, and stratigraphic maps coding Mayville, Burnt Bluff, Manistique, and Engadine layers take on rainbow qualities made of patterned rather than colored streaks.

In *Geology of Michigan*, Dorr and Eschman point out that U. S. 2, the east-west highway running across the southern edge of the UP, "crosses the eroded edges of all the Silurian formations of that region, from the younger one near the Straits, westward through the oldest." Exposed fossils are all "of marine types. Corals, brachiopods, and bryozoans are especially common." Extensive quarrying of Silurian dolomites and limestones northeast of the Straits, at the UP's eastern end, includes "[o]ne of the largest dolomite quarries in the world." In Michigan the Escarpment is less often a feature of parks, recreation areas, and nature preserves than in Wisconsin or Ontario, but it can be traced across the Upper Peninsula at memorable locations.

To continue along the arc of the Escarpment, I start where boundary water islands, like steppingstones, led me, on the Garden Peninsula of Michigan, headed to places on the Upper Peninsula of which almost none of my earlier travels there made me aware.

10

In order to follow the arc of the Escarpment from Wisconsin into Michigan, without ferrying from the Door Peninsula to the Garden Peninsula, we drive north up the western side of Green Bay, cross the border over the Menominee River, and continue along the shore to Escanaba, where we spend the night, and in the morning leave early so that we can stop at Rapid River Falls Park on our way. Beyond a bridge over the Rapid River, we pull into a parking area. The sun has come out, and so have fierce and energetic swarms of mosquitoes. Walking across a wet field to the river's edge and gazing at the falls with challenged concentration, we flail away at mosquitoes all the while.

The falls are a series of low ridges the river tumbles over, the water frothing yellow with forest tannins. They offer evidence of erosion over a section of Ordovician strata west of the furthest strand of Silurian strata. I'm reminded of various strands of strata arching around the UP, beyond one another in older and older strands to the west and northwest. It's helpful to sort out the strata, if only in a cursory way. Here, where the river carved its channel through Ordovician rock layers, I appreciate seeing what preceded the Silurian range we'll move into shortly, even as the mosquitoes shorten our visit and make us scurry back to the car.

Back on US 2, we head east past the north ends of Little Bay de Noc, the Stonington Peninsula, and then Big Bay de

Noc. The bays, named by French explorers for an Algonquian tribe encountered here, the Noquets, are short fingers of water opposite the long stretch of Green Bay to the south. Illustrations of Upper Peninsula strata claim the Stonington is Ordovician in origin. Further east, the stubby Nahma Peninsula at the north end of Big Bay de Noc is variously labeled as either Silurian or Ordovician or, in one case, as shale rather than as dolostone.

I'm sometimes confused about stratigraphy when I compare sources: in Wisconsin the lowest, earliest layer of the Niagaran series is the Mayville Formation, with the Burnt Bluff Group, the Manistique Formation, and the Engadine Formation rising successively above it, but in Michigan, various sources subdivide those layers into additional formations. One source presents the Nahma Peninsula as chiefly Mayville, another as chiefly Manitoulin. Nomenclature will likely change in Ontario and New York. The 1999 Geologic Time Scale of the Geological Society of America uses none of these terms in any study of the Niagara Escarpment I've read. I decide to settle for locating sites where terms are familiar and where what I expect to see will look very much like what I've seen before. In the Upper Peninsula I know I will be near places—Burnt Bluff, Manistique, Engadine— that once gave names to Niagaran strata.

We pass Big Bay de Noc and turn onto the Garden Peninsula, following M-183 south through Garden and on to Fayette. The west side of the Garden Peninsula is the most pronounced edge of the Niagara Escarpment on the Upper Peninsula, poking down into northern Lake Michigan and separating Green Bay from the lake just as the Door Peninsula does in Wisconsin. Its shoreline is jagged on either side, a series of inlets and bays separated by promontories of varying length and sharpness. The western shoreline has three prominent bluffs: the shamrock-shaped Garden Bluff midway down the peninsula, between South River Bay and Garden Bay; the stubby Middle Bluff further south across Snail Shell Harbor from Fayette State Park; and Burnt Bluff near the southern end, between Sand Bay and open waters around the Grand Traverse Islands.

The parking area and the Visitors Center at Fayette State Park are high above the historic site of Fayette, on the escarpment walling off the curved finger of land that forms Snail Shell Harbor. In spite of drizzle, we set out on a portion of the Overlook Trail, a path through cedars on an escarpment ledge. If not for the fog, we might be able to see the Stonington Peninsula across Bay de Noc, but we can at least overlook Snail Shell Harbor and the restored remnants of the mining community. In the distance to the south, beyond that harbor and the spit of land where the buildings stand and across Sand Bay, I see the outline of Burnt Bluff. A photo in *Geology of Michigan*, taken approximately from where I'm standing, inserted arrows along the top of the bluff to point out the Glacial Lake Algonquin shoreline and, nearer the tip, the "uplifted cliff and concave terrace carved [. . .] by higher waters of one of the immediately post-Algonquin Glacial Great Lakes stages." Those features make me feel more familiar with this setting.

The Overlook Trail heads roughly north along the Middle Bluff, past higher sections of the bluffs further inland, all well weathered. The forest is thick with beech and maple but also has prominent stands of cedar. It's often difficult to see the thin layers of dolomite, likely Manistique Formation, through the shadows and the foliage and the accumulation of leaves and needles. The trail doesn't stay close to the edge and when we lose the sense of being on the bluff, we turn back. The raised sections often appear to be peeling away, and chips rather than slabs litter the talus beneath them. Only once do I see a massive multi-layered slab of dolomite tilted at a steep angle where it had collapsed from undercutting.

On the way back, we pause to gaze down on Snail Shell Harbor. From the edge of Middle Bluff I can see the open ground amid the trees where the historic mining town was laid out and the inlet off the harbor where boats still tie up. Some buildings less devoted to smelting and commerce are barely visible in the trees at the head of the spit. From this perspective the town seems ephemeral, almost toy-like, with

the buildings overshadowed by the trees, the cleared land so small against the foreground of the harbor and the background of the bay and the distant pale blue bulk of Burnt Bluff.

* * *

In *The Fourth Coast*, Mary Blocksma reports, "Fayette State Park smells of cedar and fir and lies so quiet on the harbor, I can hear a sail luff, but once it was so clang-bangorous here that the church, the school, and many of the homes were built at miles' remove." In their Upper Peninsula guide, Mary Hoffman Hunt and Don Hunt note that "soot and smoke, noise, mud, horrible smells, and stockpiles of materials made one visitor compare Fayette unfavorably to Cleveland's worst slums" and picture "soot-covered children breathing air so dirty wives couldn't hang out wash to dry." In the 1880s, nearly 500 people worked here, the majority close to the smelting operation, the managers further from it.

Fayette Brown, Jackson Iron Company general manager, chose the site because of plentiful forests to fuel the blast furnaces, plentiful Niagara Escarpment dolomite to purify molten iron in those furnaces, and open passage from Escanaba and the iron range beyond into Lake Michigan and lucrative markets. Once forests were depleted and more economical smelting and steel-making methods developed, Fayette struggled as a company town. In 1959 the property became a Michigan Historic State Park, its crumbling ruins preserved and made tourist-accessible. Fayette serves now as a semi-pristine homage to nineteenth-century industry.

In his guide to Michigan's parks, Tom Powers claims, "Fayette, without a doubt, is the most picturesque village, deserted or inhabited, in Michigan." Mary Blocksma finds the "stark, restored village, oddly immaculate" evocative: "A massive stone building with rectangular towers and arched windows that resembles an ancient cathedral [. . .] Scattered round, charcoal kilns look like big brick beehives. The remaining buildings are weathered wood, stark and rectangular, including a severe, gray-planked hotel that looks haunted." Fayette combines restored and preserved buildings with a scrubbed emptiness, making it a place someone interested in regional or industrial history can visit without fully reproducing its actual former life as a company town that, in its heyday, most of us would have wanted to avoid.

Along a gravel road downslope into the restored village, signs inform us what buildings once stood on what is now open lawn or tree-filled depression or low protrusions of foundations. Wooden structures are weathered and gray, stone structures lack roofs and windows. The slope leads to the bay. There's a symmetry to the smelting complex above the harbor, long low buildings at either end, spacious and empty, separated by two tall cubical blackened towers tapering as the shafts rise up. Inside one building, a grilled iron gate closes us off from ashes and rubble piled at the bottom of the furnace. Through the grilled gate on the opposite side of the rubble light enters the space from gates on four sides. Like industrial obelisks, the towers are capped with low metal pyramids and light doesn't stream down from above.

Through open arched doorways the view of the Middle Bluff on the north side of the harbor lures me outside to drift below the blackened towers and past a brick beehive charcoal kiln across the grass and through the birches toward broken spears of pilings at the water's edge. The Middle Bluff is high and formidable, almost leaning forward above a narrow slab-layered shoreline. The forest, grown back since the end of the smelting, is thick atop the bluff; somewhere close to the land end is the remnant of the quarry from which stone was extracted for all these buildings. I can see openings in the long, gray bluff, shallow caves and niches, vertical crevasses, as well as the varied shades of its strata and its narrow talus beach.

In "The Geology of the Niagara Escarpment, Fayette, Michigan" Timothy M. Dellapenna calls this "the largest exposure of the Middle Saurian Burnt Bluff and Manistique Groups," the Burnt Bluff Group just above the Mayville Formation displayed so much in Wisconsin. On geologic maps, the Burnt Bluff and Manistique Groups run up the western edge of the peninsula and the Engadine Group occupies its remainder. Middle Bluff reminds me of Pottawatomie Point

on Rock Island, Boyer Bluff on Washington Island, Table
Bluff on the Door Peninsula, and I settle for knowing that
massive wall of stone is Silurian in origin and continues the
Arc of the Escarpment.

We backtrack into the village. Half its twenty buildings
are open to the public, more visitors have entered the park,
and a tour is in progress. We amble among and apart from
others to investigate the buildings: the roofless company
store, the boarding house, the hotel, the machine shop, some
residences. Eventually we drift out along the harbor.

Snail Shell Harbor lies between a narrow curl of land
and Middle Bluff. Two large sailboats are tied up along a
long wooden dock. West of the shore the land rises. Some
residences are partly hidden in the trees and accessible from
a quiet path circling into them with open views of the bay.
At the very tip of the curl, an open, windswept picnic area
offers a sweeping view of the bluffs and the harbor and the
village.

To most of the early residents of Fayette, that long mass
of dolostone may have seemed like a reassuringly unlimited
supply of flux to purify the iron ore in the smelting furnaces,
but surely some of them were awed by the scale and the
antiquity of Middle Bluff. Certainly, that's what keeps me
looking back as we walk up the road out of the park.

* * *

Fairport, a fishing community at the tip of the Garden
Peninsula, is eight or nine miles south from Fayette. No one
is around when we pull off the road to reach the shoreline.
Having gazed north toward the island chain linking the
Escarpment in Wisconsin to the Escarpment in Michigan,
I feel obliged to gaze south towards it while I have the
chance. But here at lake level, there's nothing close to an

elevated overlook. In the haze of distance we barely discern the outline of Little Summer Island on the horizon. Portions seem scarcely above water, so low and tentative, and I see only an unbroken swath of trees, a thin blue line above the deeper rumpled blue of the lake and the bright green of the shallows immediately offshore.

Remembering the kayaker who crossed these waters and our cruise past many islands in the chain, I hoped for a closer view of the northernmost islands. Now, reluctantly, I settle for having seen what I've seen as I've seen it. By reaching the tip of the Garden Peninsula, we're as close to Wisconsin on land as geology will let us get. State boundaries don't represent what geology and geography tell us the land is doing. We turn back north in Michigan, as if we've jumped off the last of those islands onto the mainland again, ready to follow the arc of the Escarpment across the Upper Peninsula.

11

A sign in Sherry's Port Bar endorses Fayette as "A town too small to have a town drunk, so we all have to take turns." We stop there for lunch on our way to Manistique, thirty miles northeast of Fayette Historic State Park. We drive up the western edge of the Garden Peninsula, cross the lower section of Hiawatha National Forest, and curve northeast along Lake Michigan into Manistique, at the mouth of the Manistique River.

In the nineteenth century, Manistique prospered as both a fishing port and a distribution point for the trees the Michigan lumbering industry sent down the Manistique River. Now (in the twenty-first century) it relies on sport tourism and the popularity of a nearby casino, one of five in the UP run by the Sault Ste. Marie Chippewa tribe. We may be the only travelers in town searching for the Niagara Escarpment. Glimpses of Silurian stone are visible in road cuts or in an abandoned quarry off the roadside. We head for the one that formed Quarry Lake, in the center of Manistique.

Manistique Central Park is a sprawling complex, with sport facilities for soccer, baseball, basketball, tennis, archery, hockey, skating, and sledding. Its lake is a water-filled quarry with visible walls and a half-mile long footpath lining its kidney-shaped circumference. The narrow, shallow north-end section has a small sandy beach. The waters are deepest in the eastern half, where the quarry was most thoroughly excavated.

We circle around to a parking area and stroll down to a wooden lookout deck for the long view of the lake's east side. Stone walls rise as much as ten feet above the water, though considerably lower in some places. Their surface is rough, uneven, and weathered, more crumbling and broken up at the north end. Evergreens line the top of the wall in various sizes and small shrubs are sometimes rooted in the talus close to the water's edge. Near the overlook, where the wall is the lowest, the stone is particularly weathered. Beneath the bright green water rough tiers drop off quickly. In places the lake is fifty feet deep.

Remembering the bluffs at Fayette Historic State Park, that high wall of stone exposed to view by glaciers and lake waves, I realize that quarry walls were once exposed here to a similar extent, in depth rather than in height, by commercial excavation. We're on top of the cuesta, with no scarp visible. The industrial equivalent of a scarp, the quarry walls that once revealed a portion of the Manistique Group of Silurian strata are here mostly submerged below recreational lake waters. The rim of layered stone above the water serves more as a retaining wall for the lake than as an indication of how thoroughly the strata was quarried. Beyond the Garden Peninsula I am more apt to find portions of the Escarpment in what lies below the surface than in what rises above it.

At the Upper Peninsula's southern shore, the cuesta slants beneath the Michigan Basin, here below Lake Michigan, to the east below Lake Huron. Vistas here differ from those at Middle Bluff or Door Headlands. We drive to the Lake Michigan shoreline at the rounded southern tip of Manistique. The Manistique Boardwalk through Carl D. Bradley

Memorial Park on a narrow strip of land is nearly two miles long, arcing through stony wetlands and beaches. We stroll out and back in a cold, brisk wind. Offshore, a breakwater offers access to the Manistique East Breakwater Light, a red obelisk stark against the sky.

Here, east of the Garden Peninsula and its matching Door Peninsula, we face the length of Lake Michigan. If we sailed due south, it would take a while to reach the western coast of Michigan near Sleeping Bear Dunes, sixty or seventy miles away. In that distance, the Niagara cuesta would sink ever deeper below the Michigan Basin, beneath the Devonian and Carboniferous depositions at the northern tip of Michigan's mitten and later depositions in central Michigan—beneath thousands of feet and hundreds of millions of years of more recent strata. North and west of us is the Escarpment's geologic past; south of us is the continent's geologic future. In a lighter, warmer breeze we might stand there in contemplation longer than we do.

* * *

In the past, whenever we hiked or camped in the Upper Peninsula, we steered toward the northern coast, either to the Keweenaw Peninsula and Isle Royale, or toward picturesque places like Tahquamenon Falls, Munising Falls, Pictured Rocks, and Lake of the Clouds in the Porcupine Mountains. Every time I unfolded Michigan maps to refresh my knowledge of UP routes or scanned tourist folders we'd collected from state visitor centers, I'd see the name Kitch-iti-kipi and wonder whether to detour to see this "Big Spring" that ranked among essential sites. We never did. But now that the Niagara Escarpment dominates my sense of what sites are necessary, it's prominent in our itinerary.

Kitch-iti-kipi, the Big Spring, in Palms Book State Park, is about a half-hour's drive inland from Manistique, on the western shore of Indian Lake. Indian Lake is large, six miles long by three miles wide, with sizable state parks perched on its southern tip and up its west side; Palms Book is small, taking up a mile of shoreline on the north side of an elbow on the lake's northwest corner. Unlike those other parks, it lacks campgrounds and beaches, features only a concession store and picnic area, and centers simply on the Big Spring.

The parking lot and the picnic area are both busy. To reach the spring we walk a short winding trail through cedar forest, the trees tall, the forest floor open and devoid of under-growth. Other people bustle around us, coming and going from the dock where the raft is moored. We take up space at the end of a short line. The dock is empty and closed off, the raft presently across the pond. In green water close to the dock, submerged tree trunks jut toward the spring's center, lime coated and pointed. The pond bottom near the shore is dark green with accumulated leaf litter but further out seems gray and mostly clear of debris. Kitch-iti-kipi is two hundred feet wide and forty feet deep, the largest freshwater spring in Michigan, gushing over 10,000 gallons of water

 a minute, and the slow progress of the raft across the pond and back allows plenty of time for passengers to look around, gaze into the deeps, scout the shoreline.

The raft slowly approaches, guided by a cable stretching across the spring. We all stand aside to let its passengers disembark, then file onto a roofed wooden vessel with sturdy railings and solid frame, roomy and open. A long rectangular opening in the center provides a view beneath the vessel at the depths of the spring, though looking through it into clear water, you have little sense of its depth. A large wheel in one corner is mounted on that cable and almost anyone can set the vessel into motion. Some boys are eager to crank the wheel and start us across—but don't seem much interested in the spring itself. I make my way back to a place where I can gaze at the calm surface of the water, the green of the surrounding forest it blurrily reflects, and the brighter green at the bottom of the pond. Then I find a spot by that center opening.

A sign there explains that the water comes from rainfall and snowmelt seeping into the ground through glacial till along a layer of interbedded dolomite and shale that lies beneath a Burnt Bluff layer and flows above a series of shales. The water "moves slowly downward, dissolving soluble components of the bedrock, creating caves and tunnels"; it "is pressurized as more and more water seeps into the bedrock from the surface." The Big Spring is above cracks in the Burnt Bluff strata and pressurized "water squirts into the pool through a dancing layer of sand." It's that dancing sand that most of us try to spot as the boys cranking the wheel send us slowly across the spring.

The noonday sun casts the raft's shadow across the pool bottom. We are sometimes torn between watching our progress across the pond, the opposite shore slowly growing closer, and watching the rectangle of shadow darken succeeding sections of the floor. We all attend to the shoreline forest's nearness as we draw close, but on our slow return I concentrate on the depths. Abundant trout swim lazily beneath the raft while below them, parts of the spring bottom bubble and roil, circles of gray sediment churning in waters rising from the dolomite. These are the vents replenishing the spring, invisible from the shoreline but continuously flowing. The pond floor is forty feet below but, in the clear water, the circles of moving water that the vents displace seem somehow near. It's hard to tell how large the trout may be and difficult to guess how close to the surface they are.

Midway across the pond, I look up from the depths long enough to peer at the wide winding stream that sends this water half a mile down to Langes Bay of Indian Lake. Thick forest shades either side of the stream and its surface seems no more disturbed by its flow than the placid surface of the pond. At a distant bend the stream disappears. Opposite the stream, we're near enough to the shore we started from for me to see the encrusted tree trunks that lie suspended below the water. As we dock, I realize that, below the trunks, I can see the dolomite walls of the pond.

We shuffle off the raft and off the dock, past an equal number of people waiting to board and crank themselves across Big Spring. Strolling slowly through the cedar shade along the path, I cast my thoughts back earlier in the day, to our viewing Quarry Lake in Manistique Central Park. I suddenly remember that the first quarry I'd seen converted to recreational uses was also called Quarry Lake, in Menomonee Park in Wisconsin. A logical choice to name a pond formed from commercial excavation of the earth. I thought too of the flooded floors of other quarries, non-recreational pools created by rainwater and snowmelt.

Something there is that doesn't love a man-made hole in the ground. Whether repurposed deliberately or accidentally, these lakes and pools remind us of industrial impacts, both historical and contemporary, shaping the landscape. In either case, when we think of the Escarpment, we can't help thinking of what isn't there, of what's been removed and what else is allowed to fill its space.

At Kitch-iti-kipi, in contrast, I keep thinking about the natural processes that formed the spring, processes millennia old and still in operation. This is one way the earth creates its ponds and, to comprehend it, I have to understand the strata under my feet, the strata below which the water flows and through which it spouts upward to roil the spring floor. Water and rock engaged and interactive, reminding me that the cuesta is something more than simply the strata behind the scarp.

12

Past the Garden Peninsula, the southern shoreline of the Upper Peninsula dips and arcs a long way east until it reaches across a long stretch of open water to the almost triangular St. Ignace Peninsula protruding into the Straits of Mackinac a relatively short distance from the tip of the Lower Peninsula. For those canoeing Lake Michigan's northern shoreline from the Straits, as Jean Nicolet and his party did, a likely place to shelter was a small point extending into the lake.

Stories about how this point was named vary. One version has French voyageurs call it "*seul choix*," "the only choice"; another credits a distortion of an Ojibwa word, "*shashoweg*," "the straight line". Contemporary Michiganians pronounce it as "Sis-shwa." Ignoring my college French, I practice the local pronunciation on the way to the Seul Choix Point Lighthouse, just over twenty miles east of Manistique. I expect the shoreline there to be similar to the one near the Manistique Breaker Light, but since the point is a more pronounced finger of land, it may offer a better sense of the Cuesta sliding under the lake.

The Seul Choix lighthouse, a white brick column with decorative overhanging window arches and stone ribs supporting a metal catwalk below the lantern room, rises over seventy-eight feet high. Built in 1895, it was maintained by lighthouse keepers until 1972, when it was automated. The

Michigan Department of Natural Resources purchased it
and leased it to Gulliver Township. A museum run by the
Gulliver Historical Society occupies the adjacent fog signal
building, and outbuildings and grounds are well tended.
After gazing at the tower, we head through the trees for
the shoreline.

At the point's southern edge, we emerge onto a broad,
flat, rock beach. The rock surface is uneven but otherwise
uniform except for abundant shrubs and grasses growing in
crevasses and frequent spots where deeper indentations have
been filled with either lake water or crunchy white shells.
We weave our way across the rock surfaces toward the water,
finding more evidence of eroded strata, broken chunks of flat
rock lying in the small pools or in the midst of the shells.
Dark mosses spill over cracks and fractures and small yellow
flowers occasionally find root and rise a little way above the
rock. Just offshore, glacial erratics appear above the waves.
It's an overcast morning and the waves match the grayness
of the clouds and the grayness of the rocks.

In an online satellite view of Seul Choix Point, the shoreline appears almost striped. The tree line is all round green
growth and then the coast loses color. A narrow strand
of dark gray runs along the tree line, the surface we first
encounter, with scruffy growth interrupting the solid rock
surface. Then a wider strand of white parallels the dark gray,
with pockets of green shrubs dotting the white. Then the
gray of the waterline forms the next strand. From overhead
the slabs of rock are clear, often fractured or jointed, jagged
at the edge where submerged rock is evident. The lake is
bright green near the shoreline, a contrast to the green of
the tree line and the darkening green of the waters further
offshore. The colors of the lake provide a sense of its varying

depths and the distance below the lake the Niagara Cuesta soon slopes.

Where the rock surface is most uneven and the depressions most pronounced, I squat down and consider what the elements have exposed. Some rocks broken from the cuesta are rounded and smooth, having undergone considerable weathering in Lake Michigan waves. Other rocks are almost neatly formed, flat on top and bottom, mostly straight on the sides, as if chiseled off the strata. On a small scale, they resemble the larger slabs in the talus below cliffs and bluffs elsewhere along the Escarpment, wherever the scarp face is prominent. In places where I step off the continuous surface into rubble and shells, I see the exposed edge of the rock and the tight layers of strata that built up over time to form the cuesta. The edge of the rock seems as neatly cleaved as the walls of a quarry or a cliff face. Remembering the satellite view of the coastline, I wonder if, should I venture offshore, I would see an escarpment carved out of the cuesta rising above the lake bottom.

Sue and I slowly circle the point, sometimes pausing to watch waves rolling in, offshore erratics resisting them, clouds drifting slowly above the lake. From time to time, we trudge over huge mounds of white shells, so thick and dense they bury the rocks, adding another layer of strata to the coastline. On the eastern side of the point, we ascend an opening in the trees to an open, grassy area bordered in places by lilac bushes in partial flower.

In the large lot with a boat ramp where we parked, other vehicles have arrived while we were on the beach. Men are geared up in wetsuits and prop surfboards unloaded from rooftop carriers against their vehicles. My images of surfing are mostly west coast ones as well as, more recently, memories of our grandson surfing the Florida Gulf coast; Lake Michigan never struck me as a promising body of water for surfing. While others carry surfboards off toward the shore, we stroll over to men still getting ready.

I wonder aloud how the lake could be deep enough for surfing. The men explain that, though the near coastline is only ten feet deep, further offshore it becomes 40 feet, guaranteeing good waves when the wind blows north up the lake in summer. Sue asks about the shells on the beach; there seemed to be billions of them. Those are zebra mussel shells, they tell us, washed in by the same summer waves that make good surfing. In other times of the year, they are deposited profusely at the southern end of the lake, on the Indiana shoreline. We thank them for the information, wish them good surfing, and trudge glumly back to our car, while images of those mounds of zebra mussel shells compete with images of the exposed cuesta we came to see.

The zebra mussel is a persistent and prolific invasive species, an Asian mollusk brought here in the ballast of international freighters. Over several decades they've spread widely to deleterious effect on native mussels and fish, interrupting the food supply of larval fish by filtering microscopic plankton from the water, smothering native mussels, and clogging water intakes for utilities. They reproduce rapidly, have no natural predators in North America, and attach to one another in large clusters. The NOAA website claims, "As many as 700,000 zebra mussels have been found in only one square yard of surface area on boats, pilings, and pipes." Their presence has caused the decline of commercially fished species, including lake whitefish.

Crunching across the empty mussel shells, I first felt only mild irritation at being distracted from examining the cuesta that centuries of wave action might have exposed. But driving away from Seul Choix Point, I think of the oldest rocks on the shoreline being coated by the remains of a recent invasive species. I sometimes enjoy traveling back in time in my Escarpment encounters, transporting myself back into the Silurian or at least into the period after the last glaciers receded. The memory of walking on mussel shells keeps me anchored firmly in the present for much longer than I'd like.

* * *

U. S. Highway 2 runs most of the length of the southern Upper Peninsula, beginning in the west at Iron Mountain, on the mainland border with Wisconsin, passing through Escanaba, and extending east for 143 miles as far as St. Ignace, on the north end of the Mackinac Bridge. Road cuts occasionally expose Silurian dolostone, and attentive drivers rolling north, away from the lake and toward the center of the peninsula, detect an upward tilt. If you think the Escarpment is an arc, its cuesta always angling down toward the Michigan Basin, and its scarp always facing away from it, as it does dramatically in Wisconsin, you might logically assume that climbing north on the cuesta in Michigan would similarly lead to an escarpment.

I sometimes made such an assumption and once asked Donald Mikulic, a Senior Paleontologist at the Illinois State Geological Society who spoke often about the Niagara Escarpment, where he had seen such a bluff in the Upper Peninsula. He replied that, while such a bluff may be hidden somewhere in the UP's deep woods, he never found one no matter where he wandered. Those bluffs along the Garden Peninsula—Burnt Bluff, Middle Bluff, Garden Bluff—were the best sites to see the Escarpment in its expected form.

Later, Eric Fowle of the Niagara Escarpment Resource Network, who has traveled the entire arc, confirmed Mikulic's judgment on the basis of his own wanderings. I was unlikely to blunder onto a scarp anywhere in the Upper Peninsula.

But walking the shoreline at Manistique and Seul Choix Point made me pay more attention to the Niagara cuesta. To the south beyond Seul Choix it disappeared under Lake Michigan and, eventually, under Michigan itself, but to the north and northeast it continued to rise. To gain a deeper sense of the cuesta, I charted a course beyond Highway 2, deeper into the woods of the Upper Peninsula.

13

An industrial tour of the Niagara Escarpment could move easily from quarry site to quarry site. The UP's southern shoreline displays prominent quarries along its length. Fiborn Quarry is one of several sites deeper in the interior, about sixty miles northeast of Seul Choix Point. George M. Ehlers' *Stratigraphy of the Niagaran Series of the Northern Peninsula of Michigan* includes a map of the entire UP and other maps running county by county which indicate Silurian formations: Mayville, Engadine, Burnt Bluff, and Manistique. On two maps, Fiborn Quarry sits squarely in the Burnt Bluff portion of the strata. Online, the quarry is a large light gray blob in the midst of seemingly endless deep green forest. I rely on road maps to get there, but I'm often uncertain where we are, even when we're on Fiborn Quarry Road.

At the end of the nineteenth century, William Foresman Fitch and Chase Salmon Osborn ("Fiborn" blends their last names) saw potential in the site, built a railroad spur into the property, began quarrying in earnest in 1905, and later sold the business to the Algoma Steel Corporation, a Canadian manufacturer. It went through periods of intensive activity or production lulls depending on the market for steel, high during World War I and the late 1920s, low during the post-war recession and the Great Depression. At one time a village composed of a boarding house/meeting hall, a number of family houses, a grocery store and post office, and a school was established around the site. The population rose and fell with the company's fortunes. In 1936, the quarry closed, its machinery was dismantled and removed, and only the shells of the railcar building, the powerhouse, and the crusher foundation were left standing on the quarry floor.

Since 1987 the Michigan Karst Conservancy has maintained the site as the Fiborn Karst Preserve, along with two other sites in the northern Lower Peninsula. From May through October conservancy members spend one weekend a month working on trail upkeep and leading tours of the Hendrie River Water Cave; they close off the cave from mid-October to mid-May for hibernation of the Little Brown Bat and Northern Long-eared Bat. According to their website, they "conduct scientific research and educational programs at all three preserves, covering geology, hydrology, biology, and history." The website provides information about the history of the quarry, the features of the preserve, and the nature of karst, with historic and contemporary photos and illustrations, and links to downloadable trail maps.

My awareness of karst as an underlying feature of the Niagara Escarpment makes the Fiborn Karst Preserve a necessary stop in the Upper Peninsula. The notable features of karst terrain are cracks or crevices in the earth, sinkholes where steady seepage has dissolved portions of limestone or dolomite below the surface and allowed the surface to settle lower, and caves created by enlargement of underground passages. Such terrain creates particular habitats for animals and plants, and also creates contamination problems where agricultural and/or industrial pollutants seep into community groundwater supplies. As the Conservancy points out, "Groundwater in karst areas can flow faster than 30 feet per hour, meaning pollutants can travel 10 miles in only a week." Particularly in well-populated areas, an understanding of the relationship between geology and hydrology is important.

The roads around Fiborn Karst Preserve are generally rough, better suited for an SUV or a truck than a four-door family sedan. We drive a sedan. At the Preserve's southern access, after contemplating the two-track dirt road through thick woods pockmarked with water-filled dips, we elect to walk in. We soon reach more open ground high above the quarry floor and get our first look at what we'll be descending onto. A vast gray open space, sporadically interrupted with scrubby trees and shrubs, is crisscrossed with roads, and often ponded. Distinct piles of rocky rubble dot the landscape. In the distance a stone building juts above low trees. We arrived at the opposite side of the quarry from the northern trailhead on Norton Camp Road and its pavilion of information kiosks. We stand at the midpoint of the Barbara Ann Patrie Memorial Trail, a 1.5-mile loop running atop the western wall of the quarry and back across the quarry floor.

We descend a steep rubbly track into the quarry to follow the road winding roughly northwest. The landscape is unlike others we've been on, those quarry floors scraped almost smooth across underlying strata. The surface is gravelly and rocky. Rock piles, formed from scraping away overlaying soil (overburden), rise intermittently above flat ground and separate low, often water-filled depressions. The shallow ponds are often "solution pans," essentially sinkholes in the making, not yet having developed drainage points large enough to undermine the ground beneath them as deeper sinkholes

have, the ones where the ground has sunk lower as its underlying support washed away. The guide to the Dr. Rane L.
Curl Sinkhole Trail crossing the quarry floor names several
specific sinks and two creeks. The Flat Creek Sinkhole is
one of the steeper sinkholes on the quarry floor; Cone Sink,
not far away, was formed by the collapse of an underground
cave passage, probably a sunken channel of Flat Creek. The
Sinkhole Trail guide explains that "a 'distributary' network
of streams" can become one main stream if the "openings in
the limestone become large enough and in that case can cut a
small canyon into the bedrock." That happened at Reluctant
Sink, forming a "blind valley" sinkhole, narrow and sediment filled. In karst environments, streams like Flat Creek
and Bog Creek here can readily disappear underground,

into channels carved
out of the bedrock,
sometimes emerging at
lower levels, sometimes
vanishing altogether
into the aquifer. The
trail guide warns us at
each sinkhole to stay
back from the sides.

We drift closer to the quarry walls, distinct layers of Burnt
Bluff dolomite topped with glacial soil and a second-growth
hardwood forest and lined with fallen rock along the base.
Ahead of us are remnants of quarry buildings. The weathered
top of the ore-car building, rising above the trees, seems like
a natural formation, but past the trees we enter a lower level,
two passages side by side, each open at either end, where ore
was loaded into railcars. The ruins of the powerhouse are
behind the loading building and across the two-track from

it is the larger railcar storage building with tall rectangular openings on every wall and an airy and empty interior.

A path leads up into the woods and eventually to the Norton Camp Road parking area, where the trailheads proper begin. To return to where we started, we follow the Barbara Ann Patrie Memorial Trail through a forest of second-growth beech, sugar maple, balsam fir, and hemlock. We rise onto the western edge of the quarry and often lose sight of it in the woods, sometimes pausing to peer into deep cracks and crevasses in the quarry walls. A side loop swings us out to an overlook above Fiborn Pond, then brings us back to the main trail. It's June and mosquitoes and black flies are abundant and aggressive. We pass small cave openings with only brief glimpses into Bad Breath Cave and nearby Quarry Cave, which is thought to be the remnant of a larger cave destroyed by quarrying. The MKC website explains that, in addition to Hendrie River Water Cave and Quarry Cave, "Four other caves are known in the preserve, all small, wet and not suited for amateur explorers."

The caves here are the result of water seeping through the bedrock and sinkholes opening up enough to allow access from the surface. The most accessible is the Hendrie River Water Cave, regarded as the longest cave in Michigan and relatively young, carved since the last glacial period. It has "about 1,500 feet of mostly high, narrow passage with a stream running along the floor." At the end of the cave, "the stream sumps in a circular passage known as the Goop Loop," then it "resurges in a spring about a mile away. Lower passages of the cave are prone to flood after heavy rains."

We aren't visiting on the monthly weekend when Conservancy members lead a tour, requiring prospective cave visitors to have written permission, sign a Preserve Use

Permit, agree to wear a helmet, warm clothing, sturdy footwear, and bring three sources of light and extra clothing to
change into after leaving the wet cave. (Later, regretting not
having seen the cave, I viewed a YouTube video in which
MKC members wander through it. Its tightness and wetness
made me feel considerably less regret, and the video itself
gave me a sound, even satisfying, sense of the karst caves
below the preserve.)

We emerge from the woods onto the open rim where we
began and take in the expanse of the quarry one last time.
On the way back through the trees, we talk of karst and
sinkholes and caves, but in very little time no longer feel
the presence of the vast open space that emerged from the
woods an hour or two before.

* * *

Other than shoreline cliffs and bluffs, the quarries dotting
the Escarpment's arc are the easiest places to understand the
layers making up Niagaran sections of Silurian strata. The
farther I travel, the more I uncover updated designations for
strata. I'd like to simplify the nomenclature, think in terms
of the Burn Bluff Group, for example, and less in terms of
the Hendricks and Cordell Formations that subdivide the
Burnt Bluff Group, and still less in terms of the Fiborn
Member of the Hendricks Formation of the Burnt Bluff
Group, which writing about the quarry and the preserve
persistently refer to.

Yet constant reference to the Fiborn Limestone suggests
something distinctive about the limestone and dolomite at
the Fiborn Quarry that made it valuable for smelting iron
ore, producing steel and later for manufacturing cement
and lime for plaster, refining sugar, and making paper. Mark
Whitney's *Fiborn Quarry, Then and Now* goes into some

depth about its development and decline and includes a chapter on geology by Rane Curl explaining the geological nature of the site, its composition, its karst features, and its sinkholes and caves. Curl claims that the Escarpment's rocks "extended over a much larger area north [. . .] well into Canada as far as Hudson Bay, but have since been eroded back by glacial scouring, rivers, and chemical weathering." He recalls the way a concentration of magnesium salts in evaporating seas partially or totally converted limestone into dolomite. "Conversion to dolomite occurred to most of the original limestone of the Niagara Escarpment after its deposition," he writes, "but a few layers escaped conversion, including most notably for this narrative, the Fiborn Limestone."

Following the final period of glaciation, channels of the Hendrie River formed at the wetland on the south side of the quarry site. Curl explains how the "acidic swamp water" dissolved the calcite in the limestone, "enlarged joints (cracks) in the rock and, over time, produced a network of underground drainage channels, a natural 'dewatering' karst drainage system of sinkholes and caves." The first mention of the future quarry site came in a report by Henry B. Brevoort Jr., a government surveyor, in 1845. In Section 16 of Township 44N, Range 7W, he walked what he termed a natural bridge between two sinkholes, noticed a cave entrance, and recorded it on his map. Near the turn of the century, Chase Osborn visited the site, discovered what came to be called the Big Cave, and "went underground in it fully 300 feet I should judge and was compelled to back out on account of the insufficient torch light." Osborn invited State Geologist Alfred C. Lane to map the surface features and caves of the section. Lane found "some small sinks, which are the entrance to several hundred feet of cave, low and flat, in general not over 2 or 3 feet high, but with a channel 6 to 8 feet deep cut in beautiful meanders." The channel stream, he learned, "falls in a cascade into a larger and picturesque sink hole about 30 feet deep, in which no outlet could be found." Lane located a river cave and reported on the purity of the limestone.

Quarrying eventually destroyed most of the Big Cave and changed the nature of the sinkholes. Today the Hendrie River Water Cave is the only one accessible. Whitney reports that two other caves exist, the Kochab Cave with "485 feet of low, wet, muddy passage" and an unstable ceiling "in danger of collapse," and Disgusting Cave, "low, almost impassable." Water still sinks into the ground. No doubt there are more unknown water passages and caves below the quarry floor.

Reading about the caves there, remembering how quickly our awareness of the quarry left us as we passed through the surrounding forest, I can't help musing about quarry history I've overlooked: namely, its original absence. I imagine what the land was like when Brevoort, Osborn, and Lane saw it starting more than a century and a half ago. They walked through boundless forest interrupted only by lowland swamps and wetlands and winding streams that sometimes disappeared into sinkholes and sometimes reemerged some distance away. Standing on the quarry rim and looking across it, it's hard to imagine that forest once covered most of that space at the same level as the tops of the walls. A great deal of industry cleared that land and then gouged a hole so deep and wide it seems impossible that it ever was full of stone and rampant with foliage. The emptiness captures your attention and diverts it from realizing that the same stone that's missing from the quarry is still there in the unmined quarry walls, the same stone hidden below your feet, the same stone undergirding the forest that stretches out in every direction around you.

In the UP I've been absorbed not by the cliff face of the Escarpment, but by the cuesta behind it—or instead of it, by what lies below the surface. The nature of the cuesta's composition lets water have its way with it, find its own way of burrowing beneath it, rising up through it, smoothing it, undermining it, changing it in slower increments over immense amounts of time. The vulnerability of karst, the roiling of springs, the persistence of waves, the ways in which constant change still maintains a presence that calls no attention to itself—all these reward awareness and concentration and willingness to be in the moment. If I pay attention as I cross the cuesta, it offers me a lesson in the balance between continuity and change.

Boundary Waters

Part Two

The Saint Mary's River flows from Lake Superior into Lake Huron between two cities named Sault Ste. Marie, the smaller one in Michigan, the larger one in Ontario, and between two countries. The borderline winds around islands where the Upper Peninsula juts into Lake Huron. On American maps, Sugar, Neebish, and Drummond islands, with some others, are colored white while St. Joseph, Cockburn, and Manitoulin, with some others, are colored green; on Canadian maps the colors are reversed. In a satellite view, all islands are the same shade of foliage green, and territoriality is indeterminate. Though the islands are in a direct curving line, Canadian St. Joseph's is plopped in the middle of three American islands and American Drummond interrupts the Canadian chain.

Maps need to be exclusive in focus. Neighboring entities only show up in fragments, like accidental portions of bystanders' bodies in family snapshots. Michigan's official transportation map cuts off most of Manitoulin Island, Ontario's official road map shows an unidentified tip of Drummond Island, and neither can avoid sections on the opposite side of the St. Clair River that divides them or many of the abundant islands near each of their borders. If Lake Huron's water level dropped drastically, all those islands clearly would be linked to one another; the St. Mary's River and the North Channel separating them from mainland Ontario and the UP would simply be lowland valleys. Of all those islands, only Drummond, Cockburn, and Manitoulin—and nearer the Bruce Peninsula, Flowerpot Island—are undergirded by Silurian dolomite of the Niagara Escarpment, a distinction most maps don't make clear. Scrolling in and out online for a closer view of an island or an expansive view of the landscape to which it belongs, I find a black line marking a border but nothing in the topography explaining why those islands belong to two separate nations.

My insistence on following the arc of the Escarpment changes my perspective. The Escarpment doesn't observe borders. When I complete my crossing of the Upper Peninsula cuesta at the village of De Tour, passing north of the Straits of Mackinac shoreline, I've driven as far east in the UP as I am able to go, just as I knew at the tip of the Door Peninsula in Wisconsin that islands awaited beyond the harbor. Here again I recognize the boundary waters and the islands above them as separate from their neighboring mainlands, embodying their own distinct geographical entity. After I visit them, I'll have crossed from Michigan to Ontario, but while I visit them, I'll see them as the unit of the arc of the Escarpment that they are.

14

Seeing it on a map, Mardi Jo Link thought Drummond Island was "shaped like a big blue crab," its claws appearing to her "as if they were trying to pinch the shore of the mainland and hold on." It's an apt description. In her memoir *The Drummond Girls*, as she crosses on the ferry, she calls the island "a sentinel hunk of rocky earth grounded in the unpredictable currents" and except for "a ferry dock and a limestone quarry, its coastline looked uninhabited." With waves breaking on a boulder-strewn shoreline, trees swaying in autumn color, and evergreens crowding an inland hill, the island appears to her as "almost timeless, like a prehistoric continent modern life had chosen to leave alone."

Niagaran dolomite can be found across the length and breadth of Drummond Island. On the west coast just south of the ferry dock, the Drummond Island Quarry reportedly ships out a million and a half tons of dolomite annually. The Soo Locks were constructed of it. On the east coast, Marble Head, a stubby thumb of exposed Escarpment overlooking a shallow shoreline and nearby Cockburn Island, has rocky shelves that (in Keith Taylor's poem, "Drummond Island Fossils") "step down to the lake" and offer a chance to see "limestone honey-combed with delicate/ coral branches that waved from the floor/ of an ocean we can't imagine." Marble Head and, on the north coast, Fossil Ledges are accessible by kayak along the Drummond Island Heritage Water Trail and by land down some rough, often challenging roads. The Niagara Escarpment is also exposed in an extended area of alvar, at Maxton Plains.

On the north end of Drummond Island, Maxton Plains borders the upper half of Potagannissing Bay to the south and the North Channel of Lake Huron to the north. The Michigan Department of Natural Resources Maxton Plains Management Area (4,358 acres) and the Nature Conservancy's Maxton Plains Preserve (1,210 acres) together make up the Maxton Plains Ecological Reference Area, intent on preserving the integrity of the alvar and the rare plants and animals occurring here. Maxton Plains blends features of Arctic Tundra, Great Plains Grassland, and Great Lakes Habitat. It includes white cedar conifer swamp, boreal forest of balsam fir, white spruce, and aspen, bedrock beach along the shoreline, and isolated patches of Great Lake marshes. The Nature Conservancy's website claims that the site preserves eight Michigan state rare plants, like prairie smoke and Houghton's goldenrod, and attracts over 160 species of birds, including "such rare and threatened species as the upland sandpiper, osprey, northern harrier, [and] sharp-tailed grouse."

The alvar is the preserve's most striking feature, making the deepest impression. The Nature Conservancy asserts that "alvars found on Drummond Island are the largest remaining high quality alvars in North America," "a globally significant alvar landscape"; in large bold-faced letters it points out that "Alvars are found only along the Baltic Sea in Europe, northern England, northwest Ireland, and the Great Lakes." This is a major location where it is found along the entire Escarpment.

* * *

Because we've been to Maxton Plains together once before, Sue elects to stay in Cedarville and catch up on work, while I drive off to De Tour Village, 22 miles east, to catch the 7:40 ferry to Drummond Island. I'm aware of the Niagara Escarpment most of the way. Cedarville is a jumping off place for Les Cheneaux ("the channels"), thirty-six islands of varying sizes lining up near the northern shoreline of Lake Huron and perched on Silurian strata. Some five miles east, the road passes through a portion of a quarry at Port Dolomite, a huge enterprise shipping several million tons of dolomite each year. Mere glimpses from my window impress me with the scale of the excavation here, which one source refers to benignly as a "dolomite harvest."

I am the only one in motion eastbound and only two or three others pass westbound. The evening before, at the Mainsail Restaurant in De Tour, we enjoyed the best white-fish we'd ever eaten. Half a dozen cars are already in line to board the ferry and soon we roll on board. On this July morning the air is cool and the sky a little overcast, but the ferry ride across the De Tour passage is calm and shipping traffic light. As we dock on the island around twenty-five minutes later, the sky brightens and clears. A long line of vehicles waits to take the ferry back to the mainland.

It takes three-quarters of an hour to reach Maxton Plains from the ferry dock, crossing nearly half the island east and then two-thirds of the island north. I encounter no other

traffic most of the way and, once past the more populated area, even pass two women in shorts and tank tops blithely walking down the middle of the opposite lane. By eight-thirty, at the end of the gravel section of the road, Nature Conservancy signs bleached almost beyond legibility explain the alvar landscape of the Maxton Plains Preserve.

Scraped and scoured by glaciers, in 10,000 years the terrain never built up a soil layer more than 10 inches thick. As the Nature Conservancy notes, "flat and horizontal plates of bedrock are exposed—giving the impression of, and earning the name, 'pavement' or 'limestone pavement.'" Plants find purchase only in the cracks and joints of the pavement; those that flourish tend to be either tundra or prairie plants and flowers. Winters here can be hard and long with fierce and insistent winds. Some trees amenable to such conditions, like aspen, fir, and spruce, grow where they can at the borders of the alvar.

If you think of the Escarpment mostly in terms of precipitous bluffs, jagged precipices, or craggy karst caverns, the flatness of Maxton Plains will take a moment to adjust to. In *The Drummond Girls,* Mardi Jo Link claims that she and her friends "were struck silent" by the sight when they came to the plains.

> Before us was an ancient place, a flat circle of silver and gold a half mile across and surrounded by florescent evergreens. The silver came from the concave, unbroken expanse of flat rock under our feet, so damp with dew, fog, or mist that it gave off a metallic sheen. The poplar leaves, the grass blades, the yellow of fall-blooming wildflowers, and even the wings of birds and insects merged together in the sun, creating an airy layer of gold.

The passage conveys a proper impression of what you see on the plains, not only in certain light but upon reflection as you try to take in what exactly you're beholding. To me this morning, it seems a very large space to be the only person in, though I quickly realize I'm not completely alone.

Driving slowly west from the crossroads to get my bearings, I soon startle (and am startled by) a deer in the middle of the road. I slow even more to let her take her time prancing into the grass. Shortly afterwards I slow again to let two sandhill cranes cross in front of me, then another mile further see another deer's backside moving away from the road and two more cranes strutting close to it. Coming around a curve between two thickets of trees, I spot a rabbit sitting motionless by the road, as if waiting for me to pass. While not entirely indifferent, none of these creatures seem concerned about a stranger passing through their neighborhood.

I continue west until I see no more open space, then wind my way through thick forest into an area near the western coastline. I park and walk past a large double row of huge round boulders to a marshy shoreline. Half a dozen geese are wandering through it. A few scruffy trees stand in a line a little inland from the rocky beach; in the channel between the beach and a distant tree-lined shoreline, boulders protrude above the water. The shallows here and the grasslands across Maxton Plains are dotted with glacial erratics, making me appreciate once again the shoreline dangers for navigation.

Returning from the preserve's westernmost edge, I slow often to gaze at more pairs of sandhill cranes stalking the higher grasses. They move with deliberation and concentration and I'll eventually see seven or eight pairs almost evenly spaced on either side of the road. Sometimes I hear white-throated sparrows in the distance, their song always invoking northern forests for me. I don't hurry to get back to my starting point.

From time to time I leave the car and walk out into an open space where the flatness and the growth on the alvar are evident. I step lightly, keeping to rocky surfaces. At one point, where thickets of trees line the way on either side, the road widens and its surface is entirely a bare patch of alvar, the limestone pavement that everyone refers to. The joints in the pavement look almost industrial, manufactured rather than natural. If not for the grasslands and trees around it, the space could pass for an urban parking lot.

In other places the alvar pavement is nowhere near as flat and clear. I come upon rough patches where wind and weather have made the surface less even and gravel has blown into the indentations. In such places lichen have gained a foothold and hang on tenaciously.

I drive east beyond the information kiosk, stopping at places where I can look across a wide stretch of grassland interrupted only by glacial erratics of considerable size, some as large as my car. Again and again in the grasslands bare patches of stone appear, as if in all these centuries the grasses and shrubs have never been able to secure a footing there. In the distance the grasslands are fenced in by rows of mixed conifers, spruce, fir, and red pine. When I detect movement in the grasses, I discover more pairs of cranes and stand for a time to watch them, as if I hadn't seen any others all morning.

Two more cars have parked at the information kiosk. From my perspective, they seem very small and isolated against the backdrop of Maxton Plains. Recounting her visit here in *An American Map*, Anne-Marie Oomen writes of driving "out to where the surface of the world changes, or rather where there ceases to be a surface as I understand it." She sees the alvar here as "a revelation of the planet itself," "an epidermis of earth, a limestone layer scarred with the geometry of glaciers." It takes some intense concentration to comprehend what we're seeing here across the alvar plains. I envy the cranes their innate, instinctive understanding of where we are.

*　*　*

Waiting for the ferry back to the Upper Peninsula, I step to the side of the dock and gaze off at the Drummond Island shoreline, the water clear enough for me to see the rocky shelf below the quiet waves. I'm aware of how, as traversing the Wisconsin Escarpment had, my crossing of the Michigan Escarpment has brought me to an island again and will send me across other islands in order to reach another mainland. For a moment, I consider how different this island is from those that surfaced in the Lake Michigan boundary waters and remember how different the Escarpment in the Upper Peninsula is from the Escarpment I know so well in Wisconsin.

Halfway around the arc of the Escarpment, I'm gaining a renewed sense of its continuity as well as a deeper appreciation of its mutability.

15

My drive to Manitoulin Island takes me north from Lower Michigan to the Mackinac Bridge, across the Upper Peninsula to Sault Ste. Marie and into Ontario, then east to Espanola, paralleling the North Channel. The landscape of northern trees and waterlogged lowlands resembles UP terrain but becomes rockier and more jagged nearing the turn south off the Trans-Canada Highway onto Highway 6. The approach to the Niagara Escarpment changes perspective, not from younger Devonian and Carboniferous strata but from older Precambrian and Ordovician strata. The difference is striking.

As Shelley Pearen explains in *Exploring Manitoulin*, Highway 6 "runs from the granite and quartzite Canadian Shield landscape of the North Shore to the limestone lands on Manitoulin, two landscapes adjacent yet extremely different in terrain and vegetation." I travel down the length of the La Cloche Peninsula, mostly owned by the Whitefish River First Nation, an Ojibwe community. The route onto Manitoulin crosses Birch Island, which Pearen identifies as "the junction of the ancient northern Precambrian shield and the younger Paleozoic rocks of the La Cloche Peninsula and Manitoulin Island." Its highest visible peak is called Dreamer's Rock, a large granite boulder once climbed by Indian youth in search of cosmic insight.

While there are Precambrian rocks north of the La Cloche Peninsula and Ordovician rocks on both Great La Cloche Island and Manitoulin's northern shoreline, Cambrian Era strata from between the Precambrian and the Ordovician is missing, a considerable *unconformity*. Crossing the North Channel from the Ontario mainland to Manitoulin Island requires a leap across a 53-million-year gap in the geologic record.

The route from Whitefish Falls on the La Cloche Peninsula to Little Current on Manitoulin runs amidst islands of every shape and size scattered through the North Channel in either direction. It's easy to recognize how, except for high water, all these islands are part of the same land mass.

Manitoulin's shoreline is sharply and persistently indented with long bays stretching toward either one another or the opposite side of the island. On the east shore, only a narrow strip of land prevents Manitowaning Bay and South Bay from turning a large portion of peninsular land, now the Wikwemikong Unceded Indian Reserve, into a separate island. On the western end of Manitoulin, the distance between Bayfield Sound and Lake Huron is very short. Higher lake levels in the past made Manitoulin a series of distinct islands. A figure in *Manitoulin Rocks!*, a thorough and accessible geology book, shows the island at three different stages: in the high water Lake Algonquin stage 11,000 years ago, only a few separate outcroppings rise above lake level; in the Lake Nipissing stage 5,000 years ago, much of contemporary Manitoulin is exposed; today (due to lower lake levels) the island is somewhat larger than in the Nipissing stage, but the authors claim that "9,000 years ago, it was almost twice as large as it is now." Even now, it may be the world's largest freshwater island, but rising water levels could force sections of it to secede and become islands on their own again.

Manitoulin Island is a good place to think about the changes time brings to something so solid as the Niagara Escarpment.

* * *

Driving south past the Sheguiandah First Nation, I stop briefly at Ten Mile Point, where a commemorative plaque informs me of a Jesuit mission that stood here in 1648-1650, serving "the Algonkian-speaking Indians of Manitoulin and the North Shore of Lake Huron." The number of First Nation sites on the island make cultural history unavoidable on Manitoulin.

The bluff I stand on is Ordovician in origin. In *Manitoulin Rocks!*, an outline of the island's eastern end confirms that its highest part is in the north and east and the lowest part is in the west and south. Illustrating the expected orientation of the Niagara Escarpment and the Niagara Cuesta, the bluffs face away from the Michigan Basin and the cuesta slopes into the Great Lakes. Here, Silurian strata has been eroded down to the level of Ordovician strata and then lower lake levels eroded away the Ordovician. The Niagara Escarpment on Manitoulin Island will be found further inland.

Once, returning to mid-Michigan from enjoying Shake-spearean theatre in Stratford, Ontario, my wife and I circled Lake Huron to the north rather than cross the border near its southern end. From the tip of the Bruce Peninsula, we took the ferry to Manitoulin and drove up the island's eastern end. We stopped at High Falls, a well-known site, but because it was late summer, the falls weren't falling at all, not even a trickle. Now in spring, I'm on Manitoulin again, optimistic about winter thaw and spring rains. When

I reach the High Falls Rest Area, the High Falls are gushing, making clear how its gorge was formed.

A steel fence prevents access to the falls, but the gorge walls still show the effect of powerful runoff over millennia. Large flat slabs of dolostone sprawl on one steep slope and a multi-layered section from the opposite wall lies at its bottom. The sapping process is evident in the protruding upper layers of limestone and the recessed layers of shale below. The lip of the falls, 30 meters (90 feet) high, is sharp, smooth, and straight. The two largest talus pieces on either side of the pool reveal how deeply the supporting strata must have been eroded before the overhang gave way. Where the creek disappears into woods on its way to Manitowaning Bay, I see how deeply into the Escarpment the brook has carved this gorge.

I head for a higher perspective of the north coast. South of Little Current a steep winding dirt road takes me to McLean's Mountain Lookout, a long flat picnic area facing north. At 328 meters (1,075 feet), the view is broad, panoramic. The North Channel is dotted with islands, West Bay is open and wide, and the La Cloche Mountains line the distant north shore. With binoculars I pick out buildings on some islands and some structures in Little Current. Clouds are thick and in constant motion, changing the light minute by minute, suddenly illuminating rock faces on the far hills that were in darkness a moment before. Behind me, wind turbines turn briskly.

Calling Manitoulin a "continuation of the Niagara Escarpment," Shelley Pearen describes the island as "a huge limestone rock formation which is tilted down toward the southwest where it slides into Lake Huron." The east end is its highest side and Highway 540, which winds west along the northern coast of the island, "follows the base of the Niagara Escarpment, the edge of which is marked by sharp northern coastal cliffs." I set off west, in search of the road between the town of Honora and the M'Chigeeng First Nation at the tip of West Bay that will lead me to Cup and Saucer Hill, the foremost example of Silurian strata. Pearen terms it "breathtaking" and "the most outstanding example of the Niagara Escarpment on the island." At 352 meters (1,155 feet) its summit is the highest point on Manitoulin.

From a parking area on Bidwell Road, across a kilometer of private property, the Cup and Saucer Trail starts a persistent climb, often over steep and rocky terrain. The name Cup and Saucer comes from the formation of a small rock hill on top of a larger flat-topped hill, dating back to the highwater levels of Lake Algonquin some 12,000 years ago, when the hilltop was a little island all on its own. The Escarpment itself stretches for several kilometers and faces the eastern end of the island. A side trail, the Adventure Trail, leads to a narrow rock chimney and a climb on wooden ladders. At many points the hiker can step to the scarp edge —free of protective fences or walls—and gaze off across Manitoulin.

Soon after starting on the trail, in dark woods, I am arrested by the sight of a huge round erratic. A small indentation on the side and a long indentation arcing below it make me pause and examine what looks like a nose-less face in stone, all glacier-sculpted. As my cellphone warms up for a photo, a man whose black hair and clothing matches an SUV near the trailhead thuds down the trail that the boulder faces and encourages me about the shortness of the climb. I set off briskly, checking the rocks and glacial debris on the trail. Flat stone surfaces are scarred with glacial striations, and other stones tip up from underground, exposing both strata and scars. Short towers of escarpment strata stand beside the path. I pay strict attention to uncertain footing when scrambling over a steep section lined with rocky out-crops and tree roots, past tall cedars. Eventually I reach a level where the blue beyond the trees tells me I'm near the top of the bluffs.

I wander slowly, pausing often at openings and vistas, gaining the most vivid perspective on the face of the bluffs and taking in the overwhelming vastness of the panorama before me. In the distant rolling skyline of varying high-lands to the east, occasional dots of white in a palette of greens remind me of human presence, the long low vivid blue of Manitou Lake opening the forest to sky. From time to time I'm able to look along the escarpment toward more exposed and towering scarp faces. When I see a flat slab of stone extending out over jagged layers, I recall how often the image of Cup and Saucer I've seen has shown two men talking on the brink of a tabletop-flat lip extending over a sheer white cliff. As always on Escarpment bluffs, I'm both awed and unnerved by the precipices I stand upon.

* * *

The relationship of many little lakes and a few large ones to Manitoulin's bays suggests that during millennia past, when water levels were higher, they all were one long body of water. Everywhere in northeastern Manitoulin was once a distinct island cut off from the rest of the island, most of which was entirely submerged.

At Kagawong, where Kagawong Creek plunges over Bridal Veil Falls, a low fence separates the parking area from the edge of the gorge and a metal staircase topped by a narrow viewing platform leads down into it. From the overlook, I see the breadth of the falls and the pool below and a woman on the stony shoreline taking photographs. I descend to the stairs and a trio of young women start to ascend. The photographer sets off on a trail along the creek, and I step to where she stood for my own photos, trying to figure out what I'm taking in.

Bridal Veil Falls is 20 meters (65 feet) high with a wide flat lip. The arc of the bluff is far wider than the width of the falls. A second waterfall, narrow and tepid, drops over a section several yards away, the remnant of the millrace diverted from the creek for a mill constructed upstream. A stretch of grass and shrubs and a dry series of indented layers of dolostone between the two falls separate them. The sapping of the underside of the falls has carved out a good deal of room behind the falls, including a rough ledge above the gravelly talus at the pool's edge.

A motorcycling couple comes down the stairs, immediately crosses the rock-strewn shallows, and clambers up behind the falls. They pose on the brink, arms in triumph, while a second couple take their picture from the overlook. Then that couple descends to join them, and both couples disappear behind the veil of water. Soon the trio of young women returns and, after one dawdles barefoot in the water, they too make their way behind the falls. By the time the motorcyclists leave, yet another couple arrives. The space behind the falls seems irresistible. I step carefully and get a little wet on the fringe of the falls but also edge fully behind it.

Here, almost at the deepest part of the cliff, above a short slope of rocky debris, below layers of strata edging their way toward a point almost even with the lip of the falls, I appreciate the incrementally relentless power of sapping.

Positioned near the inmost point of the cliff's curve, I gaze up at the straight edge over which the creek plummets, then off to the point beyond the water where the arc straightens into the gorge wall. How much time and how much water did it take to carve out the place where I'm standing? How much sand, sediment, and stone have washed away out into Mudge Bay?

I step cautiously out from behind the waterfall. A few people stand where I had been earlier, deciding whether to cross to where I am. I try looking cheerful without seeming cavalier and smile a greeting as I pass them.

* * *

To find places where the cuesta slides into Lake Huron and to gaze toward Drummond Island, which I won't see, I travel west along the southern shoreline, trying to be thorough about tracing the Escarpment's arc.

Near Meldrum Bay, a North Channel resort village almost at land's end, I turn off on Mississagi Road. A fork in the road would take me to LaFarge Canada's gigantic quarry, the starkest, whitest space on the whole of green Manitoulin. The road skirts the quarry, veers off into the trees, and winds some six kilometers down a gravel lane to the island's westernmost tip and the Mississagi Strait Lighthouse.

The Mississagi Strait makes a convenient passage from the safety of the North Channel, shielded by that chain of large islands, out onto potentially more turbulent Lake Huron. The 1873 lighthouse stands solidly upon rocky bluffs, its tower 28 feet tall above the lantern room. It was automated in 1970, became a historic site in 1983, and had only five keepers in the nearly hundred years it was maintained. Now, through the Manitoulin Tourism Association, it is staffed by local families.

One lighthouse keeper, according to his son, "carved a miniature lighthouse and a miniature Griffon (the ship was carved out of the beams of the '*Griffon*' shipwreck)." The *Griffon*, constructed by the Sieur de La Salle near the Niagara River in 1679, sailed through Lake Erie, Lake Huron, and Lake Michigan to Green Bay, loaded furs from trade with Indians, and on its return to Niagara, disappeared. It is the shipwreck that Great Lakes divers have longed for most. That the lighthouse keeper was carving a miniature model out of wood from the original vessel suggests that the *Griffon* sank in the Mississagi Strait. However, I've read stories about finding the ship in Death's Door Passage, in Georgian Bay, and near the Straits of Mackinac. Like some sort of holy relic, the *Griffon* haunts the imaginations of treasure-seekers over three hundred years since it disappeared.

The workhouse/visitor's center and the lighthouse are both open but devoid of people. Wandering through the lighthouse, I find empty or near empty rooms with an occasional bed with wire springs or a chair, signs of water damage on some ceilings, and debris scattered in and around the solitary bathtub. A sign on the tower stairs asks visitors not to climb them. Outside, the exterior seems newly sided and restored and looks well cared for.

I stroll around trees and undergrowth to the shoreline. Weathered benches perch above an exposed rock coastline. A very old photograph taken from offshore shows well-dressed tourists thronging the shoreline and lining the railing at the top of the tower and men in rowboats at the water's edge. Massive chunks of rock pile on top of one another, revealing layers of cuesta. Huge sections have separated from the mainland, and at the edge I hear the constant glug and gurgle of waves over submerged scarp in gleaming green water. The surface of the bluff top is alvar, fractured and jointed, both deep and shallow slashes cutting into it. I gaze across the Mississagi channel at a long dense expanse of green, Cockburn Island, the one between Manitoulin and Drummond. I sense a chain of connection back to the Upper Peninsula and the westward trend of the Escarpment's arc.

*   *   *

At the Visitor's Center for Misery Bay Provincial Park, on the south shore of Manitoulin between and around both Misery Bay and Mac's Bay, volunteers from the Friends of Misery Bay (who like to say that "Misery loves company") are sprucing up the place for the coming summer season. According to my reading, the Misery Bay Trail on the western side of the park crosses a fragile wetland on a sandy path to "the largest open alvar pavement in the park" and the sight of "glacial beaches, alvars, glacial boulders, rare and interesting plants, glacial striations, grykes and erratics." But a volunteer tells me that the Misery Bay Trail is closed today because the water level is so high that I'll find it at hip level if I try to wade across. Luckily, there's alvar elsewhere at Misery Bay.

I set off through thick forest on a sometimes rocky, often sandy trail until I emerge into an open stretch of alvar where trails divide. A boardwalk over low wetland leads me to the beach on the east shore of Misery Bay where two women sit on camp chairs close to the water while two men work on a roofed seating area nearby. They point at the Misery Bay Trail trailhead sign standing in pool of shallow water and the flooded stretch of beach beyond it and recommend following the Coastal Alvar Trail coast south and then circling back on the Inland Alvar Trail.

The path is fairly indistinct on the shoreline, sand giving way to rounded cobbles and occasional boulders, both on the beach and offshore. It briefly leads away from the shoreline onto a flat open area of alvar surrounded by sand and scruffy grasses. Shallow grikes break the pavement in almost uniform rectangles, the clints seeming as if laid down in an orderly fashion. Closer to the water again the shoreline is all sloped alvar, a light brown submerged pavement rife with karren, those round pits that dot the clints. I strain to see how far out into Misery Bay they stretch. At times the alvar is darker below the water and, where rocks have emerged at lake edge, sections near the water line sometimes seem almost bleached white.

Further on, the pavement is again replaced by cobbles and rocks, and then the beach gives way to faulted rock masses  like those at Mississaugi Lighthouse. They take some scrambling to cross over. At times the shoreline becomes a mass of thick, pitted slabs of rock, with no beach available. The rock is rounded and, except for those tiny holes, smooth. The grikes here are deep and wide with bright green water sometimes at the bottom of the joint. Sections of the rock seem to expand the closer to the bay they appear.

On the way back, the Inland Alvar Trail runs through a forest of conifers and low shrubs and often opens up in broad areas of alvar. Some are rough and weathered, lined with patches of lichen and moss and scruffy grasses; some are smooth and almost systematically divided by shallow or sand-filled grikes. In a few wide sunlit spaces, the pavement is rife with Lake Daisies, bright yellow flowers called Manitoulin Gold at Misery Bay.

The alvar at Misery Bay is broad, varied, and impressive, and it sticks in my mind as I return to the center of Manitoulin Island. On inland roads, I often see Escarpment strata along road cuts, and at the South Baymouth waterfront to catch the ferry, I'll see the same shoreline rocks I've seen elsewhere. But alvar too seems to be everywhere, underlying so much terrain. On the west side of Lake Mindemoya, abundant trees and shrubs grow out of exposed alvar, grikes outlining clints stark and wide. I begin to think of Manitoulin not only as an Escarpment island but also as a thoroughly alvar island.

I've sometimes described myself, jokingly, as a Great Lakes boy, but lately I feel more and more like as an Escarpment boy. Instead of locating myself in terms of states and provinces, I've begun to locate myself in regard to geology and its place in a long chain of connection. When I do, I feel more anchored to where I am wherever I am. It's a good feeling to have when where you are is somewhere you've never been before.

16

The ferry from Manitoulin Island to Tobermory, at the tip of the Bruce Peninsula, passes through a stretch of open water between Lake Huron to the west and Georgian Bay to the east before encountering the islands of Fathom Five National Marine Park. It cruises between the largest, Cove Island, with the oldest lighthouse, and smaller Echo Island, its shoreline so wracked with deep caves that mariners would sound their horns to determine their locations by hearing the echo. Some distance east is Flowerpot Island, the second largest island, the only one where visitors can be put ashore to camp or hike. To reach Tobermory's harbors, the ferry has to cross the underwater stretch of the Niagara Escarpment linking the Bruce Peninsula with Manitoulin Island; the islands rising above the surface are tips of sunken highlands.

Access to Fathom Five involves various glass-bottomed tour boats that specialize in hovering over at least 21 known sail and steam shipwrecks. Stephens and Stephens, in *Touring the Giant's Rib*, report, "One of the more legendary wrecks in this watery park is that of the *Griffon*." Near Flowerpot Island an underwater bluff of the Niagara Escarpment drops 65 meters (210 feet), creating (a tour guide suggests) a reverse Niagara Falls. After the final retreat of the glaciers 9,500 years ago, Glacial Lake Stanley (a Lake Huron forerunner) drained into Glacial Lake Hough (a Georgian

Bay forerunner) and across southern Ontario via the early Ottawa River. Walter Tovell, in *Guide to the Geology of the Niagara Escarpment*, writes of waterfalls between Fitzwilliam Island, near Manitoulin, and the Bruce Peninsula. One between Flowerpot Island and the Bruce was investigated by Jacques Cousteau. According to Tovell, "The height of these cascades was close to the height of Niagara Falls." If you consider that the island that now rises above those former cascades once consisted of four separated coral reef bluffs—independent islands themselves for a while—and that the highest point on Flowerpot Island is 180-foot Castle Bluff, the nearly 400-foot change in elevation from that height to the bottom of the sunken bluffs is pretty considerable. It strains your imagination to try to picture that scene from thousands of years ago.

The glass bottom boat that brings me to Flowerpot Island sails past Castle Bluff in the northeast corner, past both of the prominent sea stacks on the east coast, down to Beachy Cove and its small harbor. I'm grateful for the moment when the vessel slows and turns and floats above the underwater bluff. In bright sunlight and clear water, the bluff's top is a vivid green and the drop to lake bottom before it a dark aquamarine. It's impossible to gauge the depth of the bluff and nothing is visible below it, but I still imagine it stretching northwest to Manitoulin and southeast to Tobermory, the route the ferry imitates in its crossing.

I disembark and set off on the coastal trail into the woods along the Middle Bluff or *Rocher du Centre* and above the shoreline where I'll find the island's namesake features. The Flowerpots, McLean et al observe, "stand massive and improbable, in bold relief beside the clear blue waters." Both sea stacks, rock pillars shaped by waves and weathering, perch apart from the rest of the island on rock shelves once part of that underwater bluff. They are testaments to higher lake levels and the persistence of both the stone strata that forms them and the waves that separated them from the shore behind them. They are prominent enough to be seen in the island's profile some distance away.

At a trail opening I gaze down on the Little Flowerpot, *le Petit Pot du Fleur*, and the concrete cap added to it in the 1930s to prevent erosion. Georgian Bay waters fill the view almost to the horizon, where the Ontario mainland is a pale blue streak. A side trail circles around the Flowerpot and approaches it on the shoreline, across slabs of fallen dolostone and beneath an overhanging bluff that indicates

what the Flowerpot was carved out of. The recessed section of bluff and protruding overhang has the same stone strata as the sea stack. Further along that bluff is a sea cave of uncertain depth, large blocks above the  entrance jointed and uneven, more evidence of persistent process. The shelf on which the sea stack stands is lined with joints marking layers of strata and, in the shallows before the cave opening, rectangular blocks of stone lie half-submerged. The circular base of the Flowerpot looks almost intentionally constructed while the broader, heavier top of the stack seems haphazardly deposited upon it.

From the base of the Little Flowerpot, roughly 7 meters (23 feet) tall, I look north along the shoreline to the Large Flowerpot, *le Grand Pot de Fleurs*, 12 meters (39 feet) tall.

From this angle the Large Flowerpot appears to have a sculpted face upon it, looking at the lake, like a relative of an Easter Island stone head.

I step carefully over talus slabs returning to the trail. The shoreline around the Large Flowerpot is much more rugged. Higher, uneven levels of rock and fractures separating them make descent to the beach more challenging than at the Little Flowerpot. The drop off is sometimes high and sheer, the shelf before it flat and submerged in shallow water. The sea stack's base is almost entirely surrounded by water. A few people stand off on an outcropping near the base, surveying the structure that rises roughly six times their height above them. From the landward side there's no trace of a face in the stone.

I descend slowly to where others stand, looking back along the shoreline at the Little Flowerpot. It is less imposing at this distance than when I stood below it. To the north, the bluffs above the shoreline are higher and more rugged. I can discern another face in profile but I concentrate on noticing distinctions in the color and scale of the rock layers from top to lake level.

On this day two other locations I hoped to roam, a cavern high on Middle Bluff and the lighthouse on Castle Bluff, are closed for reconstruction or renovation. I continue on the Loop Trail circling the interior of the island. The trail is a little rough but manageable and gives me a better sense of the terrain, the rocks and undulating landscape through thick forest. After I pass through campsites close to Beachy Cove, I step onto a long boardwalk above the coastline.

Waiting on the dock for the return of the tour boat, I try to imagine lake waters rising above the flowerpots, scouring away at their connection to the bluffs, shaping the sea stacks in accordance with the resistance of differing layers of dolostone and limestone and shale, smoothing the shelves of rock around them, and subsiding below the top of the bluffs that link Manitoulin to Tobermory to such a depth that waters would cascade from a height almost equal to that of Niagara Falls. It's a lot to take in.

Ontario

The Ontario section of the Niagara Escarpment continues the Arc east across northern Lake Huron, southeast down the Bruce Peninsula, due south around western Lake Ontario, and due east to the Niagara River Gorge. Canadian guidebooks measure it from Tobermory, on the Bruce, to Queenston, on the Niagara River Gorge, a distance of 725 kilometers (450 miles). The Ontario stretch is the longest section of the Escarpment, the most varied in topography, and the most populous—the Niagara Peninsula between Lakes Erie and Ontario includes metropolitan cities like Hamilton, St. Catherine's, and Niagara Falls, and proximity to Toronto.

The Ontario scarp generally faces east or northeast, its cuesta generally sloping west. Near Lake Ontario, two other geological features become significant. Tovell's *Guide to the Geology of the Niagara Escarpment* identifies the Algonquin Arch as a "southwest-plunging anticline that forms the spine of southern Ontario." An anticline is an A shape fold with an arched top; a syncline is shaped like a U. The Algonquin Arch separates the Michigan Basin, centered below the Lower Peninsula and Lakes Michigan and Huron, from the Allegheny Basin, underlying much of Lakes Erie and Ontario and portions of southwest Ontario, Ohio, Pennsylvania, and New York. The Algonquin Arch flank sloping south of Lake Ontario creates the edge of the Allegheny

Basin; the flank sloping northwest into the Bruce Peninsula
creates the edge of the Michigan Basin. The Escarpment
"reaches its highest elevation,"Tovell notes, at Blue Mountain, near Georgian Bay, where it "intersects the Algonquin
Arch."

Canada's southern border shares roughly the same lat-
itude as Seattle or Glacier National Park until it rambles
southerly at the Great Lakes. Southwestern Ontario is Canada's southernmost region; Point Pelee National Park, the
narrow peninsula spearing Lake Erie, is nearly as far south
as Chicago. Ice sheets scoured this part of Ontario. As much
as 97 percent of Canada was once under ice, and most of
its terrain bears evidence of glaciation. From Ontario, the
Saginaw Lobe covered Michigan, the Huron-Erie Lobe
moved across those lakes into Ohio and Indiana, and the
Ontario lobe advanced into New York State. Lakes Huron,
Erie, and Ontario were formed by the gouging and melting
of glacial ice. Geologists have identified different lakes or
stages of different lakes, Proglacial Lake Algonquin and
Glacial Lake Nipissing prominent among them. The location of individual lobes determined where outlets for such
lakes would occur, and isostatic rebound—the rising of land
that had been depressed by the glaciers—often determined
how long those outlets would be open. Changing water
levels sometimes inundated landforms like the Bruce Peninsula and sometimes drained them. Plentiful evidence of
an ever-changing landscape can be found throughout the
Ontario Escarpment

In 1973, Ontario officially established the Niagara
Escarpment Commission "to preserve the Niagara Escarpment as a continuous natural landscape—a vital corridor
of green space through south-central Ontario." Part of the

Ontario Ministry of Natural Resources, the NEC determines how the Escarpment can be used for farming, forestry, and mining, oversees 141 parks and open spaces, and works in harmony with the Bruce Trail Conservancy. The Bruce Trail runs 890 km (553 miles) on the main trail between Tobermory and Queenston and an additional 400 km (248 miles) on side trails, providing access to the Escarpment throughout Ontario. In 1990 the Ontario Niagara Escarpment was designated a UNESCO World Biosphere Reserve and later the Giant's Rib Discovery Centre in Waterdown became its first interpretative center.

To feel solidly grounded here, I devise a table of segments and sites mentioned in four readily accessible books, reinforce it with geological and geographical research, upload a Bruce Trail guide app for my cellphone, and plan to wander the Bruce Peninsula, the Central Inland segments, and the Niagara Peninsula. I discover that names of stratigraphic layers here differ from those in Wisconsin and Michigan and often connect with those in New York. For example, the Engadine Formation of Wisconsin and Michigan is the Amabel Formation in Ontario and the Lockport Formation in New York; the Manistique Group is Ontario's Fossil Hill Formation and New York's Goat Island member of the Lockport Formation. Names of layers and beds depend upon regional locations where certain strata have been examined, and geologists argue about whether subdivisions of various formations are distinctive or should be further subdivided. Terms change across time and depend on how recently the resource was written.

I won't master technical terms an accomplished geologist would require of herself before launching into an expedition like mine, but I'll try to understand how prominent portions of the Niagara Escarpment connect with one another across the Arc. I want to be certain that, whatever they're called, the same strata stretch the length of the Escarpment. I need to know how beginning and end connect to one another and, ultimately, how they both connect to me.

17

The theme of the seventh annual Forum of the Sources of Knowledge, affiliated with the Bruce Peninsula National Park and the Fathom Five National Marine Park, is "The Great Arc: Life on the (L)edge." The subtitle plays with the term used for the Escarpment in Wisconsin; the main title takes in its entire sweep. Wisconsinites and Ontarians will share the stage, but I'll be one of only two Wisconsin people attending without a role in the forum. I drove alone through the Lower Peninsula and up the Bruce Peninsula to reach Tobermory; everyone else crossed the Upper Peninsula onto Manitoulin Island to ferry across. Attendees include a throng of knowledgeable authorities who study or promote the Escarpment from myriad perspectives: geologists, biologists, photographers and filmmakers, vintners and brewers, tourism planners, proponents of an Escarpment Geo Park across the Great Arc.

I arrive in Tobermory, check into my motel, visit the cairn marking the Bruce Trail's northern end, then drive to the Parks Canada Visitor Centre (closed—*ferme*—until next weekend) to climb the metal tower at the start of the Burnt Point Loop Trail. It provides an overview of the peninsula's forested tip, the mainland portion of Fathom Five, distant islands like Flowerpot and Cove, and the open water that ferries cross to Manitoulin. I see some of Tobermory and, in another direction, other promontories jutting into Georgian Bay.

Another man climbs the tower. We nod, eventually introduce ourselves, and both confess our Escarpment projects. Mark Zelinski, a photographer, will be showing images from his book-in-progress, *Heart of Turtle Island: The Great Escarpment*. He tells me where to visit alvar areas, such as the end of the Singing Sands Interpretive Trail. I'm already learning something about the terrain. I make my way down after a group of geologists ascend to join Mark.

The tower's aerial view of the terrain and the conversation about alvar makes me feel as if I've made an entry into the Bruce, but from now on I'll need to connect to it on the ground.

* * *

The Bruce Peninsula generally leans northwest between Georgian Bay on the east and Lake Huron on the west, mirroring the Door Peninsula. One major road, Ontario Highway 6, runs the length of the Bruce and ends in Tobermory—Americans will urge Canadians to keep just one highway up the center, rather than create two shoreline highways that encourage entrepreneurial enterprise to intrude on the environment. The widest part of the peninsula is between the points where western and eastern shorelines end, each at a sub-peninsula. The northern shoreline links Tobermory with Cabot Head Provincial Nature Reserve, surrounded on the north by Georgian Bay and on the south by an arch in the shoreline called Dyer's Bay. The shorelines of the Bruce Peninsula alternate promontories and bays their entire lengths.

From a parking area on Dyer's Bay Road, some thirty of us board a bus for a tour at the Cabot Head Light Station led by Daryl Cowell, a Canadian geoscience consultant, and David Webster, Senior Conservation Geologist with

Ontario Parks. The bus reduces traffic on the bumpy dirt road along the shoreline, the bay on one side, bluffs on the other. For a while, flat stone slabs jut into the water but soon the beach becomes entirely limestone coral cobbles and the bluffs are sometimes 60 meters (200 feet) high.

The bus stops opposite a stream running down a rocky hill, the outlet for Gillies Lake, higher up the slope. Daryl leads us up through the woods and along the stream to where water emerges from the ground. This, he tells us, is karst terrain. The water from Gillies Lake doesn't flow from an outlet stream but instead seeps down through dolostone to form an underground channel that emerges on the slope as this spring and then runs down to the bay. He once led students to the lake, put green dye in the water, and then returned to the spring to watch the water change color. Daryl believes that the lake's depth comes from a pothole vortex formed by cobbles whirling in an ancient stream and that the water at the spring penetrated shale below the dolostone, like the Kitch-iti-kipi spring.

Traveling further along the bayshore, we occasionally see prominent highlands inland through the trees—South Bluff, Middle Bluff, West Bluff. All the land between the bluffs and the present shoreline was once submerged. A side road now leads off past a rare jack pine barrens to the Bruce Peninsula Bird Observatory's Cabot Head Research Station, near where red-necked grebes migrate through in spring and fall.

We stop at Cabot Head Light Station, high above the bay, standing on Manitoulin dolostone with Cabot Head shale below it, the shale through which the Gillies Lake springs flow. The lip of the talus slope exposes a sheer four-foot-high wall of layered strata. In one stubby overhang, fifteen layers are packed together like sheets of phyllo dough, each no thicker than my hiking shoe. Far below, the shoreline arches out into Georgian Bay, the beach littered with bright dolostone slabs.

The 1896 lighthouse, replaced by a skeletal tower in 1971, is now maintained by the Friends of Cabot Head. Some of us stay to tour the lighthouse while others follow Daryl and Daniel through the woods on a winding path.

Wingfield Basin, once dredged to serve as a lighthouse supply harbor, cuts into the northeastern tip of Cabot Head. From its south side, we gaze at distant West Bluff, Middle Bluff, and South Bluff. Sea caves and sea stacks, wave-cut notches and platforms found in the cliffs at altitudes much higher (up to 80 meters or 262 feet) than the present shoreline, are evidence of shifting lake levels and an archipelago of widely separated islands during the period when Glacial Lake Algonquin inundated the area. An immense, house-sized glacial erratic, perched atop a fourth bluff, named Boulder Bluff, reminds us that all of this was once below huge sheets of ice.

As we look across the entrance to the basin at the Cabot Head Research Station, we feel a surprising shift in temperature. Wind from the bay chills us, then by coming from the land suddenly warms us. When we eventually board the bus again, I sit in the same seat I'd had before and, peering out the window, become aware of how much escarpment I'd missed seeing on the inland side while I'd been gazing at the bay on the way out.

* * *

The Sources of Knowledge Forum's motto is "Sharing Perspectives on the Natural & Cultural Heritage of the Bruce Peninsula." Earlier annual research forums focused on Bruce

Peninsula National Park, Fathom Five National Marine Park, and the natural and human history of the peninsula, all with ecological themes. This Great Arc forum expands its scope at least as far as the Door Peninsula. Pairings of Canadian and American experts speak on a range of topics: the geology of the Great Arc, karst landscapes and caves, the Great Lakes coasts, biodiversity and challenges to it, specialty products like wine and beer, and tourism and economic development. American geologist Joanne Klussendorf's keynote address covers geotourism and the Niagara Escarpment. Over the course of the forum, similarities and differences between the Door and the Bruce emerge and comparisons cast new light on old issues. Canadians are alert to environmental problems inherent in the commercial and recreational development that the Door Peninsula has undergone; Americans appreciate the extent to which the Escarpment has been protected and preserved on the Bruce Peninsula. In Wisconsin, Escarpment sites are managed as essentially separate units: features of county parks, state parks and forests, nature centers, local conservancies; the Niagara Escarpment's primary proponent, the Niagara Escarpment Resource Network, works on a small scale, relying on connections to organizations like the Lakeshore Natural Resources Partnership, an umbrella resource for advocacy groups. In Ontario, Escarpment sites are connected by the Niagara Escarpment Commission, the Bruce Trail Conservancy, and the Giant's Rib Escarpment Education Network and recognized as a UNESCO World Biosphere Reserve. The Bruce Trail essentially encourages people to walk the length of the Escarpment in Ontario—in Wisconsin its equivalent would be the Ice Age Trail—and locations like the Parks Canada Visitor Centre in Tobermory, with its fascinating museum, and the Giant's Rib Discovery Centre in the Dundas Valley Conservation Area model a potential Escarpment Center yet to be built somewhere on the Door Peninsula.

Amidst panels on "cross-border lessons and opportunities" one riveting discussion centers on the concept of a Great Arc Geopark. UNESCO's International Network of Geoparks program defines a geopark as "a territory encompassing one or more sites of scientific importance, not only for geological reasons but also by virtue of its archaeological, ecological or cultural value." The geopark would not be a new "park" in the sense of a state or provincial park but an amalgamation of existing parks and preserves and cultural features inspired by the geological setting. The Great Arc Initiative has been advocated over a period of years and the Ontario model of attention to the Escarpment seems like a solid base for expansion of the concept into Wisconsin and Michigan.

In a sense, I've been walking in the Escarpment Geopark for some time now.

* * *

In a light morning rain, a large group boards a long, pointed, glass bottomed, glassed-in touring vessel for the Georgian Bay Coast Trip. Seats either face the bow or line either side of the transparent floor, windows all around giving clear views of rain and fog. We'll cruise along the northern shoreline, sailing past a series of promontories and points, coves and inlets, and the shorelines of Fathom Five, Bruce Peninsula National Park, and Cabot Head Provincial Nature Reserve. Once, through the haze of both fog and distance, we barely make out Flowerpot Island and discern the silhouette of one sea stack. Some of us crowd onto the stern to scan the rugged shoreline—the sea caves, escarpment face, overhangs, cobble beaches—snapping photos whenever the fog lifts intermittently and timing the shutter with the roll of the vessel. Only one of my thirty photos will be fog-free. The coastline is a ghostly forest of trees, their green barely distinguishable in the gray, vague shapes growing ever more indistinct the further inland they rise, until there seems to be no inland at all beyond the most ephemeral silhouette.

Massive shards of talus line the shore; a broad cobble-stone beach surprises us. Sometimes trees hide the bluffs but most often cliff faces dominate, sometimes high and sheer, sometimes weathered and misshapen. We pass Overhanging Point, a long, thin ledge protruding many feet above the bay with levels of erosion visible in the wall below it. McLean et al, in *Country Walks: The Niagara Escarpment*, endorse hiking to the point and standing on its dolostone lip. "It is a strange but exhilarating feeling to stand suspended on a meter of rock projecting into the air 30 meters [nearly 100 feet] above the water," they enthuse. The height of such bluffs makes it hard to imagine waves ever buffeting their uppermost levels.

Other stretches give starker, more immediate evidence of changing lake levels. While the clifftops are often solid and more or less smooth, the layers below are often cracked and notched and excavated. We can't begin to notice all the sea caves, crevasses, and overhangs. Some are positioned high and dry on exposed cliff-face; others are at the water line, still open to the waves. Some caves rise to the very bottom of the cap-rock.

In the vessel, Daryl Cowell rehearses the geological history of Georgian Bay and revisits the rise and fall of Algonquin and Nipissing, the advance and recession of the glaciers. It's like cruising in a time machine, viewing the formation of the Bruce Peninsula and Georgian Bay millennia before anything in the Cabot Head Provincial Nature Reserve could have been there. The cruise reminds me that, to know a peninsula, you must see it from both perspectives, from its surface and from its shoreline.

* * *

In *Natural Landscapes of the Niagara Escarpment*, Richard Kosydar writes, "The Bruce is a region by virtue of its landscape: peninsular in nature and dominated by bedrock." While others think of the Bruce Peninsula as extending north from Owen Sound, for him it begins north of Wiarton, half the distance between Tobermory and Owen Sound. He calls the region the Marine Scarp. Having seen, despite rain and fog, so much of the Escarpment from Georgian Bay, I want to see more of the Bruce cuesta behind the scarp. Once the conference ends, after a quick tour of the Parks Canada Visitor Centre with departing Wisconsin people, I don my rain gear and backpack and set out on the Burnt Point Loop Trail to headlands jutting into Georgian Bay.

From its northern terminus at Little Tub Harbour, the Bruce Trail leaves town past the Visitor Centre and takes a clear, wide, level path to a deck overlooking Little Dunks Bay. Midway along, the path turns south, the wide, level portion ends, and blue blazes replace white ones, indicating a side trail. The Burnt Point Loop heads into the woods, and the walking gets more challenging. Flat portions of trail weave around large, exposed rocks, many flattened on top, and rain slicked. The woods are deep and thick, the trail winding, uneven, and littered with last autumn's leaves. Mosses coat the rocks and the base of trees. The blue blazes keep me on the path. In places, rock layers demonstrate that the escarpment has weathered at multiple lake levels.

The trail dips and rises through an old growth cedar forest and gradually descends toward the waters of Georgian Bay.

I emerge onto a rock-strewn beach, stumble across it, and re-enter the woods on my way to another rock-strewn beach. Across the shallows past offshore lines of rocks I see distant islands off Burnt Point or watch waves break on a low rocky promontory. Trees rise as close to the shoreline as they dare. It takes a little scrambling for me to get back on the trail. I clamber over a low wall, cross a smooth arc of exposed, pock-marked stone, circle a narrow inlet. On the shoreline I'm startled by a half-submerged line of rocks that from my angle takes on the appearance of a drowsy hippo. In the distance a long rocky shoal barely above the water line sprouts a single scrawny tree.

The return section of the loop trail takes me further inland, away from the shore, sometimes over wetlands, sometimes over ridges. Tree roots in the thin soil often emerge from underground to cross exposed stone and disappear back underground on the opposite side. Some sections of escarpment several layers thick have cedars growing out of them and around them, hemming them in. The appearance of such a section so far inland, away from the coastline, speaks to me of the long, slow, incremental process of erosion, the impact of ice and wave over millennia. Everywhere the cedars insist on rising through and above the stone; everywhere the mosses insist on clinging to them.

* * *

On my final morning, Karen at the Peacock Villa convinces me to hike out to the Grotto. And so I take the Cyrus Lake entrance into Bruce Peninsula National Park and follow the road a long way northeast to the Head of Trails parking lot.

The Georgian Bay Trail, a wide gravel path "improved" to accommodate visitors, will lead me up to the Grotto.

It is the most popular destination for park visitors but, with it being a week before the park opens, this morning I'm alone on the trail. At a bridge where a stream tumbles out of Cyprus Lake, a mallard drake floating near stony rapids takes issue with my gazing at him in a raucous flight into the wetlands. Midway along the groomed path to Halfway Rock Point and a scenic overlook, the path to the Grotto enters the woods across more rugged terrain, passing inland remnants of escarpment, thin layers of strata piled up on top of one another above crumbled stone slopes. Near the shoreline are bioherms, limestone ridges formed from Silurian coral reefs, and in the distance the Cabot Head cliffs are a vague, foggy shape.

Soon I'm above the cobble beach at Indian Head Cove, named for a clearly visible profile of a face on one point (I also see the head of a dinosaur, unmentioned in guidebooks). Waves wash over low shelves and beat against escarpment bluffs with high caves, niches, and clear overhangs above layers weathered away. I follow the Bruce Trail across the cliffs, often over uneven rock surfaces. Nearer an opening in the bluff top, the Natural Arch is increasingly exposed, its opening wide, the drop to the rocks deep. The arch is the remnant of a cave or grotto, the lake having battered away interior support for most of the roof. Water pools below the interior lip; waves strike against it and froth across it.

In some places, like Indian Head and Natural Arch, cliffs stand at the water's edge, never sheer, always pocked and indented; elsewhere the shoreline is all rough, uneven strata, loose thick slabs above dense thin layers, shrubs clinging tentatively to the cracks in the stone. Where rock has been less resistant, holes are packed with gravel the lake crumbled out of missing stone. On the trail above the shoreline the rock is bright and smooth, weaving through low bushes.

In time I reach the indentation in the shore where the Grotto is. It's what the Natural Arch might have looked like before its roof collapsed. The thickness of the bluff above the Grotto suggests that chances of an arch forming here in the next several centuries are unlikely. I move gingerly on the bluff above it, viewing it from many angles, gazing into its interior. It's a very deep, very high cave, 20 meters long and 9 meters wide (66 feet by 30 feet). Unlike most sea caves I've seen, it occupies most of the cliff face it's been carved out of. Jagged rock hangs above the entrance and massive rocks sprawl across its floor. In summer, swimmers descend to it to swim offshore and divers explore an underwater entrance in deeper waters in the back of the cave. It's raining a little now and, glancing at the wet cliff face near me and waves pounding at the floor of the entrance, I decide not to climb down and wander around the Grotto. Instead, I survey it and recall the Natural Arch and remember seeing nearby Overhanging Point from the bay and indulge myself in a few moments' pondering of time and mutability before I continue on.

The Bruce Trail is rough and twisting all the way down to Boulder Beach, a cobblestone and broken slab pile between Georgian Bay and Marr Lake, a much smaller lake fed by Horse Lake through underground passages flowing through the dolostone and emerging as springs. In turn, Marr Lake drains through the boulders into the bay. This morning it is entirely hidden by fog. I stumble across Boulder Beach, stepping carefully, balancing like a novice tightrope walker. Karen advised me that cellphone reception would be unlikely out here and, if I broke an ankle, I would simply have to wait for another hiker to come out and find me. Having seen no one else out here since I left Head of Trails, I tread prudently.

The mist gets heavier, the wind brisker. The Marr Trail follows the Marr Lake shoreline over increasingly rocky ground, then rises up a boulder and cobble strewn chute. I climb over pitted, uneven tiered slabs, descend onto a flatter, muddier path, and eventually rejoin the easy Georgian Bay Trail. Except for three snowshoe hares, I spent the morning alone. I don't know whether seeing the Grotto and the Arch and the Georgian Bay shoreline with a host of other hikers and vacationers would have changed my perspective on them, but they may be all the more memorable when you see them in mist and solitude.

18

The Bruce Peninsula is a jagged finger of land roughly 106 kilometers (65 miles) long, its width varying, three distinct sections demarcated by places where bays or coves pinch the land. The northernmost segment runs from the tip to a potential isthmus of around 8 km (5 mi) between Isthmus Bay, a Georgian Bay inlet north of Lion's Head, and Stokes Bay, a Lake Huron inlet north of Black Creek Provincial Park. The middle segment runs from that line to another from where Colpoy's Bay cuts even more deeply from Wiarton to the Huron shoreline. "Peninsula," I recall from high school Latin, is really "pen + insula," "almost an island"—if Colpoy's Bay were dredged to open a channel across to the west, as happened with Sturgeon Bay on the Door, the Bruce would be similarly islanded. The south-ernmost section runs between that imaginary line to one between Owen Sound (the city) on Georgian Bay and Southampton on the lake, essentially Highway 21, 36.6 km (22.7 mi). South of that highway, southwestern Ontario spreads out ever wider and includes a thumb-shaped mass east of Owen Sound (the city) on the south shore of Owen Sound (the sound), down to the tip of Georgian Bay.

Various writers divvy up the Ontario Escarpment similarly. Stephens and Stephens in *Touring the Giant's Rib*, Richard Kosydar in *Natural Landscapes of the Niagara Escarpment*, and the Bruce Trail Conservancy all designate that northernmost segment (excluding Manitoulin and/ or Flowerpot Island) as the stretch between Tobermory and Wiarton, Kosydar labeling it the Marine Scarp, the Conservancy calling its chapter there the Peninsula B. T. C., and the Stephenses subdividing the Bruce into North and South Loops.

The Marine Scarp label works well to include the Georgian Bay bluffs and I'll see more heading south into the middle segment. But sites between those imaginary Isthmus Bay/Lion's Head and Colpoy's Bay/Wiarton isthmuses will let me explore different but distinctive features across the cuesta and concentrate on ways stones of the Escarpment interacted with the rise and fall of lake levels and the advance and retreat of glacial ice sheets.

* * *

To hike the Gun Point Peninsula, I find the McCurdy Access Trailhead in Lion's Head to take the Bruce Trail out to Lion's Head Point. At first the trail is flat and the woods mostly young, but I soon pass mossy outcroppings on a muddy path through overgrown and dense forest understory. Where the escarpment surface has been uncovered, the trail is often rocky. Trillium, absent further north, is abundant here. I wind through a long stretch of birch and then a tight defile with dense mats of moss and occasional small ferns on thick layers of rock. I pass fractures and joints and grikes deep into the subsurface and recognize some mossy stones as glacial erratics rather than broken remnants of escarpment bluffs. Fallen, broken sections of birch drape over boulders, and surrounding mounds are higher, more plentiful, with deeper troughs between them.

McLean et al write, "The Gun Point peninsula has the greatest concentration of potholes anywhere in Ontario."

A short side trail leads me to the Giant's Cauldron, a 10,000-year-old pothole almost free-standing at the edge of other, higher rocks. The "cauldron" is a deep cylinder scraped out at the end of the last glacial period by melt-water swirling hard granite rocks around softer limestone. After the trail descends paralleling high escarpment bluffs, another short side trail offers a climb to the top of a bluff to peer into another huge pothole. From below, where the side of the pothole has worn away, it's easy to look inside and up at the opening three meters (nine feet) above—a photo of children inside the pothole appears repeatedly on signs and fliers for Lion's Head. Other, smaller potholes abound nearby.

I continue into cooler, darker, thick cedar forest, going higher again, and soon reach a series of lookout points extolled in *Country Walks: The Niagara Escarpment* as among the most beautiful and the most impressive vistas on the entire Bruce Trail. Today the view is limited by fog, but on a clear day it would be possible to see the high cliffs at Smokey Head-White Bluff Provincial Nature Reserve across Isthmus Bay. I step cautiously to the edge of the scarp, on flat spaces between trees. Sometimes I have no indication that anything other than fog exists beyond the lip; other times I can see to the shoreline at the cliff base where dolostone slabs lie below the waves. Sometimes the cliff face is rugged and weath-ered—I find a pretty accurate image of a lion's head at one point—and elsewhere the cliff is pre-cipitous and as sheer as if

it were planed vertically. Still, somehow, where there seems to be no flat surface of any kind, plant life finds a way to cling to the cliffs. I marvel that the weathered cliff faces once were battered by waves and, before that, entirely underwater.

If I were more daring—or foolhardy—I would try to spot white cedars growing out of the cliff face, not the conveniently located cedars clinging by their curled toes to the very lip of the precipice, but members of the "ancient cliff-face forest of the Niagara Escarpment," as Peter Kelly and Douglas Larson so aptly subtitle *The Last Stand*. They also found white cedars in Wisconsin, but the most thorough portions of their research were conducted along the Ontario Escarpment, often under somewhat harrowing circumstances: rappelling down sheer cliff-faces to balance themselves precariously while boring into the cores of the trees in order to date them. Their photos are vivid and almost always taken from an angle that none of the hikers along the Escarpment will ever see. Over a five-year period, they sampled nearly 600 living trees and found nearly 250 of those trees to be exceptionally old. "Ten of these cedars were found to be over 1,000 years old," they write. "Two cedars began life as seedlings over 1,300 years ago!"

The harsh conditions the cedars face make their growth very slow. One photo shows a cross-section of a cedar tree where a penny covers decades of tree rings. The authors nickname, picture, and describe some of the ten oldest trees, dating their first years of life as far back as 688 C.E. and 701 C.E. and report that "the most spectacular and oldest cliff cedars are found on the cliffs within Lion's Head Provincial Nature Reserve." In a cluster of cedars named the Three Kings, one was 1,160 years old in 2007 (when they sampled it), another 1,037 years old. The age of the Millennium Tree, pictured with the shadow of the author hanging from a line above it, was 1,056 years; of the Snake, which seems hardly attached to a sheer cliff-face, was 1,213 years; of the Ancient One, "an awe-inspiring sight," was 1,320 years, "the oldest living tree on the Niagara Escarpment, the oldest tree in Ontario, and quite possibly the oldest living tree in Canada." The author's account of reaching the tree is suspenseful.

Unable to locate them, I picture them clinging to cliff-faces and gain more to contemplate about the time scale by which we measure the Escarpment. By comparison, making my way back from Lion's Head seems to take an immeasurably short amount of time.

* * *

St. Jean Point Nature Preserve is a narrow, jagged green spit of land jutting into Lake Huron just north of Howdenvale Bay. Its low landscape and roadside trees make its small parking area easy to miss. A path through the trees leads to the lakeshore, inundated in places, large glacial erratics strewn across the beach and offshore, the ground made up of small, broken rocks. Most of what I walk on likely gets submerged in higher waves and storms. A plover circles overhead, piping, and a loon floats calmly in gurgling, lapping waves.

Someone coming to the Bruce Peninsula might well make alvar their prime focus. Over 60 percent of the Great Lakes Basin alvars are in Ontario, some north of Lake Ontario, one on Pelee Island in Lake Erie, and most clustered in an arc ranging from Manitoulin to the southern Bruce. People at the Sources of Knowledge Forum said that alvar was everywhere around us.

One site mentioned was the Dorcas Bay Nature Reserve, part of Bruce Peninsula National Park, identified as Singing

Sands for its long sandy beach and its dunes. It also contains
fens, wet meadows, woodlands, and limestone outcrops.
A loop trail crosses a wetland near an alvar and leads to
a larger alvar near the southwest border of the reserve. At
Singing Sands, visitors hike across the beach and into the
dunes, but I arrived after two days of nearly constant rain
had flooded the trail.

A cairn established by the Sierra Club and the Canadian
Parks Service commemorated John Muir's regional wanderings in the 1860s. One display, erected for the 100th
anniversary of Muir's founding of the Sierra Club, high-
lighted "John Muir's Walk on the Bruce," calling him "one of
the first naturalists to recognize the richness of the Bruce."
It quotes his thoughts upon encountering the orchid *Calypso
borealis* in an Ontario swamp: "Are not all plants beautiful? Would not the world be poorer for the banishment
of a single weed?" Muir slogged through a tamarack and
arbor-vitae swamp, "struggling through tangled drooping
branches and over and under broad heaps of fallen trees,"
fearing he wouldn't "reach dry ground before dark." Then
he saw the solitary orchid "on a bed of yellow mosses" on
the bank of a stream. "It seemed the most spiritual of all
the flower people I had ever met. I sat down beside it and
fairly cried for joy." I'd read and written about Muir, and
sensing his past presence here created another link across
landscapes like the one the Escarpment nourished for me.

St. Jean Point, some thirty-five miles further down the
Lake Huron coastline, has no sign of sand. Stephens and
Stephens report that, despite glaciers and storms and winter
winds, the 61-hectare (15-acre) conservation area has "no
fines (sand, silt and grit produced from the wearing of the
rocks)" because its limestone and dolostone dissolve almost

entirely or disappears in the winds. The ground near the shore is mostly mucky between the large water-lapped rocks and mostly dried gravel further in.

A trail around the trees angles toward the lake through spruce and cedar to an open area of alvar. I cross large slabs of smooth rocks, scrubby plant life rising around fractures. Stephens and Stephens call this habitat inhospitable, "with temperatures that range from over 50°C (122°F) to -40°C (-40°F), with daily fluctuations of about 15°," the rock "either bone dry or covered in standing pools." They sum up the situation this way: "Cook or freeze. Dehydrate or drown."

Nearer the shore, the slabs are rough and weathered and pitted with holes, like petrified sponges. Stepping carefully over the grikes, I cross the shoreline, the rocks getting higher the farther out I go. Today the lake is a vivid blue but, noticing a white line across the horizon, I discover an offshore edge of the winter's snow and ice still lingering beyond the bay. Patches of snow can still be found in the woods.

Farther out, when four semipalmated plovers complain about my approach. I start to retrace the arduous route that brought me out, clambering over the rocks and the gaps between them. A pair of egrets stalk the shoreline shallows, and a great blue heron stands solemnly as I pass. Together with the loon and the plovers, they make me think St. Jean Point is not as desolate as it looks.

* * *

In *Guide to the Geology of the Niagara Escarpment*, Walter Tovell asserts that "the geological uniqueness of the [Bruce] peninsula lies in the glaciated dolostone pavement with the development of karst features." He emphasizes changes wrought in karst landscapes, how some caves are "formed by underground water drainage through channels in the bedrock" and emerge as springs, and others are formed when "[waves] striking the face of the cliffs, augmented by pebbles and boulders they pick up, pound away at the cliff face" and develop "hollow caverns." It depends on the stratigraphy of the individual site.

From a boat passing caves in bluffs along Georgian Bay, it's hard to tell whether their formation was internal, an underground stream eroding a passage into the bay, or external, scoured out by the battering of lake waves, or both. The Grotto, Tovell tells us, is a cave originally formed by an underground stream and enlarged by wave action. Standing above the Grotto you watch the bay work at extending the cave; in high water and storms it must be a powerful sight. Bruce's Cave, on the other hand, is a cave formed by wave action, even though it is more than half a mile inland from Colpoy's Bay and its elevation is over a hundred feet higher. The Bruce's Caves Conservation Area contains not only caves and Niagara Escarpment outcroppings, but post-glacial Lake Algonquin, which formed the caves 7,000 to 8,000 years ago, is nowhere in sight, nor is Colpoy's Bay. Beyond the thin line of roadside trees are intermittent patches of low bluff, frequently hollowed by caves and overhangs, the strata uneven and jagged. Thousands of years ago the water level in what is now Colpoy's Bay reached these heights and battered the bluffs.

The woodland trail to Bruce's Cave passes through abundant moss and lichen coated boulders and slabs that seem to have been breeding there. The moss often overwhelms each boulder it bestrides. The weathered surfaces of the boulders, rounded and smooth, suggest the impact of the waves when all this was Algonquin shoreline. It's hard for undergrowth to get a start in all that rock.

Near Bruce's Cave the terrain rises and a substantial scarp emerges. Above the trail, a light-colored stone column, darkness on either side, resembles Flowerpot Island's sea stacks. The pillar divides the cave entrance, somehow more resistant to erosion than the rock around it, so that waves circled it to carve out the scarp behind it. The talus slope contains enormous stone slabs that have slipped or tumbled off the scarp. I climb to the mouth of the cave.

Small dolostone slabs are scattered widely before the cave entrance and throughout the cavern floor. The interior walls and pillar are composed of such distinct slabs, like ill-fashioned, worn, stone Lego bricks, tentatively connected until the joints between them further dissolve. The rubble is thick and plentiful, small slabs interspersed with large ones and make for awkward, unsteady walking. Some slabs come unbalanced under a hiker's weight or hide holes or jagged pits. The cave is deep and darkens deeper in. Uneven erosion leaves shelves and overhangs along the walls and hidden cracks where the adventurous can climb through to higher, open levels of the scarp.

I step cautiously into the cave as far as the back wall and then step as cautiously back to the central pillar, all the while glancing up at the high ceiling and sensing the depth of the fallen stones beneath my feet. The joints between layers of strata are clear and uneven, hinting that the stones covering the cavern floor will continue to deepen.

On the trail back through the woods, I imagine Bruce's Cave and the Grotto switching places—Bruce's Cave on the shoreline, its floor flooded and its opening gleaming from lake waves, the Grotto up here, high and dry, surrounded by woodland, facing the slabs and boulders that recall the days when the cliff face was being beaten away to expose the cave. It gives me some perspective on the nature of the Escarpment across time.

* * *

Colpoy's Bay's deep cut into the peninsula created the narrowest point between Lake Huron and Georgian Bay. "For thousands of years," a sign near Colpoy's Lookout claims, "Petun, Neutral, Ottawa, Iroquois, and Ojibway people traveled this portage, on foot and by birchbark canoe." Later so did fur traders, explorers, missionaries, and loggers. The portage appeared on maps as early as 1657. From Wiarton's Blue Water Park at the western tip, both sides of Colpoy's Bay stretch northeast a long way and the highlands on either side resemble one another. The Bruce Trail follows the arc, down one side of the bay and out the other. On either side, the bluffs are set back some distance from the shoreline.

In a cool breeze at the edge of Colpoy's Bluff, I view the bay. Though the morning is cloudy, sunshine still casts a few bright white streaks on the bay's rippled surface, making it seem illuminated from underwater. Skinner's Bluff, the highest line on the southern horizon, is "a massive dolostone bluff," according to a Niagara Escarpment Commission landmark sign, "flanked by a talus slope of fallen rock." A long lower ridge stretching away from the north end is the shoreline of postglacial Lake Algonquin, and a still lower bluff beyond it is the shoreline of postglacial Lake Nipissing: 450 million years of change in one earthen profile.

Further northeast are low, hazy profiles of the islands at the bay's mouth: Hay Island, White Cloud Island, Griffith

Island, outliers of the Escarpment. 10,000 years ago, with the Georgian Bay basin nearly empty, they were three hills on the waterless mainland; five thousand years later, with rising water levels, they were entirely submerged, as was most of the bay's lower shoreline.

The road on Colpoy's Bay's south shore runs parallel to Skinner's Bluff. It's very high, topped with continuous forest, and clear tiers of forest along the length of its base. At Colpoy's Lookout, I look across at Colpoy's Bluff, where I'd been earlier. It seems as high as Skinner's Bluff, as tree-lined on top, and below, after cottages end, trees come down to the water. The stairstep bluffs denote shifting shorelines and lake levels. Colpoy's cliffs are lighter than Skinner's, more exposed vertically, jutting out in upright ridges, accordion-like. Otherwise, the bluffs seem like mirror images.

Surveying Skinner's Bluff, I'm struck by the depth of the overhangs in some places and the sheer straight fall of the cliff face in others. The trees atop the bluffs are darker, older than the deciduous forest below, and often trees grow straight up out of the cliff face. "Skinner's Bluff is home to part of a long green ribbon of Old Growth Forest comprised of ancient White Cedars that grow along the face of the Niagara Escarpment," the Bruce Trail Conservancy information display reports, "the oldest, least disturbed forest in eastern North America."

Rather than follow the Bruce Trail on a long, easy walk from the Bruce's Cave Conservation Area to reach the top of Skinner's Bluff, I choose to drive to the northeastern end of the bluff and hike in from there. I park near a fence behind a heavy bulldozer. Two men from a pickup truck are talking to the owner of the farm behind the fence. He points the way to the Skinner's Bluff lookouts and jokes about what he'd do with his bulldozer if I parked in front of his gate. I reassure myself—and him—about my parking and trudge off into the woods, followed shortly by the two men.

At a promontory lookout point and an opening in the trees along the bluff, we walk onto a broad pitted rock surface overlooking shoreline woods and distant bluffs. I try to memorize the view. McLean, Craik, and Sherk claim that looking to the southeast provides "a vivid sense of what the Georgian Bay shoreline looked like 11,500 years ago," when Skinner's Bluff rose above the Lake Algonquin shoreline and all the landscape below it was under water. To the southeast is another promontory, Esther's Bluff, and below it a wetland management area known as the Slough of Despond, remnant of a Lake Algonquin bay.

I continue on the trail until I face Colpoy's Bluff from Skinner's Bluff, scan the mouth of the bay and islands beyond, and sense the lake levels that once formed varying beaches and bluffs. Everywhere I walk along the Escarpment I've been aware of the scarp that fronts the cuesta, that peels away portions of it over time and makes the cuesta recede like the ice sheets that once covered it. Here, the landscape reminds me that more than one scarp can front the cuesta. Here, I can see a succession of scarps and layers of cuesta shaped by a series of lakes, islands that once were hills, a slough that once was a bay, ridges that once were shore-lines. Enduring as the Niagara Escarpment is, it certainly isn't unchanging.

19

Heading into the Escarpment area near and beyond Owen Sound, I concentrate on a variety of waterfalls and their formation. Less resistant strata below more erosion-resistant layers are weakened by periods of wetting and drying, freezing and thawing, and undermine those top layers. Weaker layers fall away, stronger layers jut out until they lose too much support and crack and tumble down and, in a slow but thunderous process, the falls creep back from the edge of the scarp, ever deeper into the cuesta, creating river gorges. Variances in depth and length among different gorges depend on the nature of the streams that form them, their ages, their volume, their constancy, and the composition of the rocks they wear away. Several streams that flow into Owen Sound illustrate in their own ways the process of falls-making, each still distinctive enough to reveal the range of possibility provided by erosion. As I follow the Escarpment, I approach them from north to south.

* * *

The Indian Falls Conservation Area rises above Balmy Beach, a few kilometers north of the city of Owen Sound and situated across from a narrow corridor of shoreline homes and Owen Sound itself. Indian Creek winds south from Bass Lake deep in the Cape Commodore Foreland and flows below a highway bridge to empty into the Sound.

The trail down to the creek bed and out to the rim of the falls is rocky and winding and close to the stream's north bank for a half mile. On this mid-May morning the creek is shallow and rock slabs rise above the water. The footpath is littered with smaller slabs and cobbles and in flood time the creek can be turbulent and deep.

The trail narrows, hemming me in between swift-flowing water and an ever-closer escarpment. Flat layers of stone in low rapids remind me that they all were once part of higher strata. Where the trail narrows enough to make walking challenging, a long wooden staircase rises up the escarpment into open forest and is succeeded by a steep set of steps worked into a further slope that leads to the top. Clearly the river has raged through the watershed in the past.

The trail winds through the woods, the forest floor gray and brown with leaf litter and barely emerging spring greens. The roar of the falls is an insistent, powerful sound. I soon glimpse it through the trees before emerging into the open. At the brim of the falls, a stream flows steadily over a table-top-flat surface. The smoothness of the stone where I stand is the creek's doing, sometime in the past, and below me the gorge has been rounded into a horseshoe shape by the water. It's a wide stream, falling 15 meters (49 feet). Behind the waterfall the sapping of the stream has exposed debris from higher layers strewn on lower ones. The top of the gorge is Manitoulin dolostone and the red layers below it are Queenston Formation shale. Debris litters the edges of the plunge pool, often in flat sheets, wide and thin. Cedars cling to the walls.

On the plunge pool's far wall, half a dozen thick layers of strata are topped by multiple thin layers of dolostone partly obscured by overhanging foliage. As the gorge winds away downstream, some walls show signs of sheer cleaving; elsewhere are jumbled talus slopes. Sometimes sizable cedars arc out of crevasses and joints.

Upstream, the southern bank of Indian Creek is open and thickly green with grasses, with a fence in the distance. The Nawash Chippewa, who had a summer village here, called the falls Drum Falls; the Indian Falls Conservation Area was once a gravel pit. But, except for that restricted view upstream and a short length of wire fencing to restrain the foolhardy from stepping to the edge of the gorge, when I look downstream and return through the woods, I have no sense of a hectic historical or contemporary world anywhere around me. I concentrate on the roar of the falls as it grows fainter with distance and on the depth and width of the gorge as I descend once more to the riverbed itself.

*   *   *

Not far into the Pottawatomi Conservation Area, due east of Owen Sound, a Grey Sauble Conservation Authority sign gives notice that the trail is a "steep rocky path leading to unprotected cliff. Use at own risk." The warning seems premature, the path through the woods level and well worn, rocks rising above the surface easy to bypass. An illustrated "Wildlife Habitat" sign invites the stroller to look for tree cavities, cliffs, caves, rocks, snakes, birds, amphibians, snags, and mast-producing trees—oak, beech, black walnut, butternut, ironwood, basswood, and the like. The path meanders through the trees, their roots spilling across the trail, and the light beyond the woods reveals the Pottawatomi River. The river flows through low rapids, rocks protruding or barely subsurface midstream, the shoreline rocky. The farther down the half-kilometer trail the narrower and rockier it becomes. The water's rush and gurgle are joined increasingly by the ever less distant tumult of the falls. In a thick cedar forest, where roots claw their way into the riverbank and the forest floor, I near more pronounced rapids. The trail and the river are near the Conservation Area's western border and a hiking path heads off into an extensive wooded area. I soon see the white patches of the main Bruce Trail, leading off either east or west.

A high arched steel mesh bridge offers an unobstructed view of a wide, swift river coming from the west and weaving first north then south near the falls. The Falls Trail leads toward a lookout point, where it ends. Closer to the river-bank, it's easy to reach trees at the very rim of the river in some places, but in others it takes some scrambling through large boulders and aged cedars. Rocks above the river are often immense and seemingly smoothed ages ago by a much larger, more aggressive glacial or even pro-glacial stream. So many of the valleys along the Escarpment were formed in that fashion. Here scraggly trees and small shrubs have finally got a toehold in the rocks and larger trees grow from the spaces between them, but even now most of the rock is bare.

The river downstream tumbles in stages into a gorge, one low lip succeeded by a slightly higher lip and then an even higher lip. Cedars stand right on the edge of the riverbank, anchoring themselves with a multitude of roots that catch at my feet as I get closer to the river. At each stage of falls, the river is further below me until I reach the precipice for Jones Falls itself. This is when I recall that warning sign. There's nothing here between the falls and the cliff edge. Even here the river plummets down a few high steps before its final plunge.

Jones Falls is 12 meters (nearly 40 feet) high and differs from Indian Falls or any falls I've seen where a stream reaches the lip of a precipice and plummets straight down. Here are multiple ledges and layers and on the opposite shore the river is obviously still wearing away the scarp it passes. At the top of the falls, in the darkness behind slim layers of strata, a cave has formed, and the river is gouging further into it as well as slicing steadily at the base of that wall. The Pottawatomi isn't done shaping Jones Falls or enlarging its gorge. The boulder-strewn plunge pool and the stark walls of the gorge downstream testify to the shaping it has already done.

* * *

Often when you visit waterfalls, you find not only a natural feature but also a historic site. Where a rushing stream promised enough power to turn a waterwheel, someone saw a chance to construct a mill and the mill became the center of a community. It happened often at escarpment sites. Some mills still exist, well-preserved; more frequently the site consists of a portion of a dam or a millrace or a stone foundation, the overgrown remains of what fire or neglect or deliberate disassembly removed.

At Inglis Falls, on the Sydenham River, remnants of former milling enterprises include two millstones used in mills that ambitious Peter Inglis began constructing in 1845 and that fire destroyed a hundred years later. The tale is told of the Governor General of Canada's visit in 1874, when a coffer dam was hastily constructed upstream in a season of low, shallow water to build up enough of a flow to impress Lord and Lady Dufferin when they arrived. It was once a highly enterprising place.

In early May, the falls need no help impressing the visitor. Stephens and Stephens report that the freezing and thawing of water in fissures in Amabel Formation dolomite generate "dynamic hydraulic forces that pry apart the stone," causing hard upper layers to break off in blocks. Inglis Falls will look quite different from Indian Falls.

At mid-morning only one other vehicle is in the parking area and a light fog is rapidly lifting. The river roars beyond a solid rock wall and paved walkways at the edge of the gorge. A high wire fence extends the limited access—at least one death here resulted from someone taking a risk. I walk to the wall to take in the view.

At Inglis Falls the Sydenham River plummets over an almost straight flat edge with a short sheer drop to the next level and then widens as it flows from level to level. It's hard to determine the number of steps it tumbles over. Huge chunks of cliff face litter the plunge pool, 18 meters (nearly 60 feet) below. The cubical blocks seem almost machine-hewn. It's hard to determine the depth of the pool. The river flows around and over sections of massive debris to reach the riverbed. Further along the wall, the mist from the falls catches the sunlight and makes the view almost fuzzy. The river cascades down an extended talus slope. The gorge wall reveals the strata the falls have worn through over eons, its base piled with immense blocks and boulders. Cedars growing out of the talus obscure the view of the riverbank and the cliff face.

Inglis Falls is on the lip of the Escarpment and the view off in the distance is panoramic. Bends in the river and luxuriant forest growth soon hide the Sydenham's course. Across the treetops a low narrow dark blue streak, perhaps the waters of Owen Sound or Georgian Bay, contrasts with the brighter blue of the morning sky. Near the lip of the falls I discern dolostone blocks surrounding the precipice and, across the bridge, see more clearly the way the river undermines the walls that enclose it and the water's turbulence before plunging over.

Across the bridge, past a closed Escarpment Discovery Centre, I walk a portion of the Bruce Trail into a certified forest—a sign confirms it is certified—and then gradually descend toward Owen Sound on a well-groomed trail. A roughly five-mile stretch of green would let me walk from the falls through the Inglis Falls Conservation Area into Harrison Park in southern Owen Sound. Across the forest floor, closer to the river, it's apparent that the forces of erosion that shaped the gorge impacted the cuesta in earlier times. Everywhere are thick horizontal layers of dolostone like those above and within the falls, the blocks sometimes separated from one another in spaces wide enough to walk through. Cedars of every size grow out of what looks to be impervious stone. The Pothole Loop Trail leads past several potholes, some deep, some shallow and debris filled, evidence of a river running across these rocks, much, much broader than the Sydenham and more powerful. The rocks and gravel that spun in whirlpools to gouge these potholes must have been in the grip of a very strong current.

In the forest, I realize, I can't hear the falls, only bird song high in the trees. I head back slowly, admiring ever more abundant trillium. I cross the bridge, scan the view downstream, then angle along the rock wall to gaze longer at the falls before I leave. The breeze carries mist from forty feet below up into my face. For a few minutes I let it.

* * *

I intended to stop at Epping Lookout simply for the view of Beaver Valley and, hopefully, the distant Blue Mountains, but discovering a sign memorializing John Muir—and renaming the site Epping-John Muir Lookout—made it even more vital. The historic plaque there claims that "Muir set out in 1864 on a walking tour of Canada West, during which he traveled much of what is known in Ontario today as the 'Bruce Trail'." He worked with his brother Daniel in a Trout Hollow sawmill on the Big Head River near a town on Nottawasaga Bay. Another display, erected by the Bruce Trail Conservancy, quotes a letter Muir wrote on May 23, 1865: "We live in a retired and romantic hollow [. ..] Freshness and beauty are everywhere—flowers are born every hour—living sunlight is poured over all [. . .]—our world is indeed a beautiful one." The sign tells us, "Viewed from high up on the edge of the Niagara Escarpment, the ancient valleys of the Bighead and Beaver Rivers tilt toward Georgian Bay," their slopes covered with magnificent forests, and bottomlands "sprinkled with ferns and mosses." It displays a map highlighting both the Bighead River and Beaver River valleys and locating prominent falls on each. Both rivers empty into Nottawasaga Bay.

Walter's Falls, northwest of Epping Lookout, is in the village of Walter's Falls on Walter's Creek, all named for John Walter who built a sawmill here in 1854. Today it is owned by the Falls Inn, a hotel and spa close to it. A viewing platform leads to a point just above the falls. Walter's Falls is a double waterfall, paired torrents plunging over the lip on either side of a substantial column of dolostone topped by distinctive fractured layers. The Bruce Trail follows the western cliff close by. The walk along the eastern side provides a glimpse of the depth of the gorge—Walter's Falls drops 14 meters (46 feet)—and the height of the western wall. To carve out such a canyon, the creek once flowed at great volume and with greater force. The Inn discourages people from attempting a descent to the base of the falls, where the creek disappears into thick woods.

The Eugenia Falls Conservation Area is south of Epping Lookout. At 30 meters or 98.4 feet, Eugenia Falls is the highest cataract in the area, flowing into the impressive Cuckoo Valley Gorge. The Beaver River is separated at the falls by a column of stone that forces the current into two channels. A stone wall running along the top of the gorge and, at either end, a wire fence discourage visitors from stepping too close to the edge, though down at the plunge pool a few young men merrily splash around. A trail to the base is recommended for only experienced hikers. (A month after my visit, a 19-year-old hiking with a friend lost his footing and fell more than 12 meters, some 39 feet, to his death. I try not to imagine his fall, but the image is too easy to envision.)

A little upstream the river rushes over low rapids, then divides at the very brink, the eastern side of the current flowing into a narrow, deeper channel scoured into the lip of the falls. The wider current is shallow and the edge uneven. Beyond the falls I see the overhang in the recess that an older river has carved and the way the gorge broadens. The talus trails down the slope beside the river and the walls maintain their height into the distance. The gorge is filled with trees that can't obscure upper portions of the cliffs, and the cliff tops are lined with a plentitude of trees, largely cedars, poised on the very edge of the drop. Cedars dominate the forest as well, often rising in the midst of—even on— exposed and weathered sections of stone. Looking back up the gorge, I see the exposed escarpment wall on either side of the waterfall, the top layer bedecked with cedars and the recesses below it uneven and fragmented.

It's hard to imagine that once there was no gorge here, no Beaver River Valley beyond it, no constant flow over the edge of the Escarpment. It's also hard not to sense the power of persistent erosion over unthinkable spans of time. This is the kind of space the earth sculpts given its own choices and its own sweet time. This is one way the earth shapes itself, one way the Niagara Escarpment reminds us that it's still here.

20

The Niagara Escarpment parallels the edge of Georgian Bay from Tobermory to Colpoy's Bay, but past Owen Sound it weaves its way across landlocked terrain farther inland. Other indentations south of Owen Sound are re-entrant valleys, once deep, wide bodies of water now channeling the remnants of rivers where waterfalls formerly provided more power and thrust. The Bighead River Valley, flowing northeast, and the Beaver River Valley, flowing east, are valleys slicing into the Escarpment and pushing its cuesta back to the west.

The Old Baldy Conservation Area is named for the exposed Escarpment cliff face above the Beaver Valley. It rises high against open sky, 152 meters, nearly 500 feet, above the valley floor—a splendid sight in full sunlight, its exposed scarp serving as a representative Niagara Escarpment cliff face. A steep "undeveloped" side road, full of twists and turns, its dirt surface somewhat loose beneath my tires, takes me to a parking area with only one other vehicle. The Bruce Trail's white blazes lead through high grasses and a shadowy forest before climbing into more rugged terrain across cedar roots and rocky outcrops. I weave through the shade below cedars near the rim of the scarp, the sky bright blue, the ground dense with cedar needles and almost devoid of undergrowth. At the bluff edge, I carefully cross uneven, mostly flat stone. Far below, at the valley bottom, sprawl pasturelands and farms and village buildings in Kimberly.

Continuing along the edge, I clamber up higher sections of the scarp. At each overlook, the vista opens wider and buildings in the valley grow smaller and treetops below are more distant. Trees cling to sheer walls in vertical profile, like determined rock climbers. In some places a broad gap yawns between the scarp's front edge and the cuesta, the Escarpment splitting itself apart; in time the front edge may either shear away and topple into the valley or stand its ground while the cuesta retreats behind it. This is how outliers form and set themselves apart from the mainland—islands close to the Georgian Bay coastline often were created this way, over immense amounts of persistent time. Sometimes I peer through such a crevice at a still solidly anchored section of escarpment. And then I'm on an overlook again, gazing across the Beaver River Valley.

From time to time, I find detached sections of strata poised among the trees away from the scarp, as if abandoned in the long history of erosion and change. Their top layer is thick and solid, resistant to growth other than moss, and the lower layers are thinner and more fragmented. They offer reminders that Old Baldy was once higher than it is now.

* * *

My aging Escarpment guidebooks are selective, rather than inclusive, about sites they emphasize; handy in specific ways, misleading in others, they can't record changes around those sites since they were published. And so, instead of a quick, direct ascent to Metcalfe Rock, a popular rock-climbing site at the edge of the Kolapore Uplands Resource Management Area, I hike in from the nearby Duncan Escarpment Provincial Nature Reserve to the west, a longer, more taxing route. Luckily, my ignorance about a different approach will work to my advantage.

A long walk on a straight dirt road down to and up from Mill Creek and then a walk in the woods takes me to the main Bruce Trail near the top of Metcalfe Rock. The higher up I go and the nearer to the Escarpment edge, the more I become aware of forces of erosion at work. Deep, wide crevices fracture the surface, some too broad to leap across, their depths not always easy to gauge as they disappear into dark caves. Cedars often rise from well within the crevices, along one wall or the other. The portion separated from the main body of the cuesta has a surface of cedar needles restraining undergrowth. Light from the open valley beyond appears behind the trees.

I stay close to the edge of the Escarpment, wherever gaps in the cuesta don't prevent it, looking off across the gorge to its opposite wall and paying attention to cedars near or below the lip of the scarp. Of Metcalfe Rock, McLean et al mention how "Cedars, twisted by the brutal elements into curious shapes, cling tenaciously to the top of the rock and, impossibly, to the sheer rock face." I haven't ignored cedars making my way along the escarpment, but I observe them closely here.

I make a winding, steep descent. Crevices lead down to caves, their depths in a darkness kept eternally out of sunlight by the forest. Trees grow up the sides of the gaps and I discern no bottom. Toward the base of Metcalfe Rock, the cliff face peers through trees clinging to it or shrouding it from below. Joints in the scarp offer wedges of darkness hinting at cave access at various levels. The cliff face is mostly a broad layer of gray dolostone, and descent beyond the scarp gives evidence of past erosion and a still deeper gorge.

A blue sign announces the 190 metre Metcalfe Crevice Side Trail, "an exciting and demanding . . . alternative route" to "Use at your own risk." McLean et al call it a "short but quite stren-

uous passage [. . .] through three chambers, each separated from the next by a steep, narrow rock barrier." I stay on the white-blazed trail.

I round the section of Metcalfe Rock that has largely separated from the portion where I hiked across the top. The cliff face is more exposed here, the fractures, joints, and crevices more pronounced, some hinting at hidden interiors. The Bruce Trail winds further down into the gorge, crosses Kolapore Creek, and makes a steep ascent up the other side, past cliff faces similar to those at Metcalfe Rock.

The trail wends off through forest and across the long wooden Mill Creek Bridge. More low, isolated outcrops of escarpment are above and below the hillside path, topped with thick layers of moss and ferns above thin, uneven layers of stone. Pinnacle Rock, identified by McLean et al as "a massive slab of Escarpment rock that fell from the cliff face," sits upended on the valley floor, its horizontal layers now starkly vertical. The trail drifts through boulders at its base and heads uphill again, crossing over into the Duncan Crevice Caves area.

Somewhere high on the east-facing scarp I step out onto an opening with an unhampered view of the valley below, plentiful woodlands, occasional farms and fields, and in the distance the face of Metcalfe Rock. Three young Canadian women from Owen Sound are at the lookout, heading out the way I've come, and one kindly opens the Bruce Trail app on her phone—my American phone gets no signal at all—to show me trails leading back to the parking area. I complete the loop slowly, pausing often to look into crevices and wide fractures, gaze into deep cave openings, and stand close to cliff-edge cedars angling out into space.

The circuit took about four hours to complete. What I've seen reminds me of the varied nature of the Escarpment: its high, sheer cliffs, its outlier-forming fractures, its deep crevices and fissures, its tenacious cedars and abundant caves of uncertain depths. It's a place where it's possible to study the Escarpment and its cuesta at length, to savor its variety and to experience both its heights and its depths.

* * *

The map of Mono Cliffs Provincial Park outlines the Escarpment and two separate park segments. Cliff sections on the map set portions of the cuesta off into individual scarps on their own. A sign calls this "the scene of the most violent natural events scientists have identified as having happened in this region" and claims these highlands "were among the first Ontario landscapes to reappear as the last glacier retreated northward some 11,000 years ago." The plain below the Escarpment formed when the Violet Hill Spillway drained a large area to the north and south of the cliffs and helped separate the long Southern Outlier and the smaller North Outlier, two ovals set off in isolation in the spillway.

The Bruce Trail runs through the park, mostly along the edge of the Escarpment but often deeper into the cuesta. The trails are open to bikers and horseback riders as well as hikers. I trudge up the wide Carriage Trail to a point where most trails intersect and climb a high, steep set of stairs to the Escarpment rim. A sign identifies unique ferns protected by the park—Walking Fern, Hart's Tongue Fern, Smooth Cliffbrake, and Green Spleenwort—and the ferns appear on the rock wall above the sign. On the Escarpment the white blazes take me north through a broad swath of woods toward an overlook with a view of a wide, green, forested landscape with intermittent stretches of grassland and at least one bright, shielded lake. Around the overlook the scarp falls away, cedars perched on its lip and rising from its crevices.

A steep metal staircase leads down the scarp face to a boardwalk perched midway along the cliff. Mono Cliffs Provincial Park insists on educating the hiker and the boardwalk takes me through a gap in the cuesta, as if to show me the interior. On either side, stone walls rise above the walkway, topped by overhanging cedars and occasionally carpeted with mosses. At times the bluff hangs over the walkway and deep crevices appear at the base. The boardwalk ends at a fenced off area above the railings, across from the midpoint of a cliff face, where I get a unique perspective, looking up at the rim, looking down at the base.

Other places where I might have accessed the depth of crevices required some scrambling and considerable caution; here I feel comfortably immersed in these fractures and able to concentrate on the walls around me. I peer past the outlying sections, toward the streambed below; I also gaze above me, at the cedars on the rim obscuring my view of the sky. I try to make the most of my time in the cliffs.

Eventually I climb out of the gap, leave the Bruce Trail, and follow the Cliff Top Side Trail as it descends toward wetlands and a junction with the Walter Tovell Trail, which runs through the park. At the north end it passes ponds and crosses a creek to parallel the base of the escarpment; at the south end it veers east near the base of the Southern Outlier. I follow it to its junction with the Carriage Trail, to exit the park, but I'm inordinately pleased to be walking on a trail commemorating the author of books and articles like *Guide to the Niagara Escarpment: With Field Trip*s that provided me with such an authoritative overview of the Ontario Escarpment. A biographical note about Tovell lists among his awards three for his contributions to the preservation of and knowledge about the Niagara Escarpment; naming a trail for him beneath Mono Cliffs strikes me as a singular honor as well, since it locates him on the terrain he did so much to preserve and explain.

*   *   *

Walter Tovell defined "re-entrant" as "Valley pointing inward from the general trend of an escarpment" and defined "outlier" as "a part of the escarpment that has become separated from it by a stream-eroded valley." I keep those definitions in mind crossing the Kelso re-entrant valley, a prominent passage for railroad and highway, to reach the Crawford Lake Conservation Area. I'll climb the Milton Outlier for a view from Rattlesnake Point. Crawford Lake and Rattlesnake Point are two adjoining conservation areas separated by a steep descent and ascent on the Nassagaweya Canyon Trail.

The trail map claims the Nassagaweya Trail, a side Bruce Trail, is 7.2 km, 10,800 footsteps one-way, and the out-and-back totals 14.4 km. It doesn't mention that amounts to 21,600 footsteps or 8 miles round trip. I'll descend the Niagara Escarpment, cross marshland, and climb the escarpment on the other side, then reverse it all coming back.

Blue blazes of the Bruce side trail lead me toward Nassagaweya Canyon where I choose the less demanding of two paths to the canyon floor. White blazes guide me across marshland on a long, solid set of boardwalks to ascend the Milton Outlier, fully appreciative of how wide the glacial spillway made the gap in the cuesta.

The climb into and out of the canyon is somewhat arduous and I am chagrined, after a long time alone in the woods, to be passed on the trail first by four mature Asian women chatting merrily and then by one cheerful family with young children. At the outlier's summit, a good-sized group relax near a place where a separate trail leads up from the canyon and a man and his son are setting up a camera to film the arrival of the man's wife, who has run here all the way from Tobermory. A woman suddenly emerges from the side trail and people start chanting "Runner, runner," but the man announces it isn't his wife. They laugh and wait again to cheer. I move through the group, someone mistakes me for a runner but is quickly corrected, and one smiling young woman chants "Hiker, hiker." I nod toward her modestly and continue past them.

The Nassagaweya Canyon Lookout on Rattlesnake Point is an open space at the edge of the Milton Outlier with a wide view of the land below. Toward the tip of the outlier are other lookouts where people can stand on the very brink of the cliffs. The canyon at the base is invisible below the flourishing forest that spreads across the gap between Rattlesnake Point and the Crawford Lake area, but I note the heights marking the escarpment opposite. To the south across the Lowville re-entrant valley, I think I perceive the outline of Mount Nemo. The outlier has been called an island of bedrock and, despite the presence of all those other people, I have a sense of its separateness.

I backtrack along the Nassagaweya Trail, cautiously descend to the canyon floor, recross the boardwalks, and take the easier path up to the Side Bruce Trail. Having looked across the canyon from Rattlesnake Point, I want to view it from the opposite escarpment. Midway back to the visitors' area, I turn onto the more rugged Escarpment Trail, rocky and rooted and ankle-challenging most of its length (2.4 km or 3,600 footsteps long, according to a sign). After passing through the woods to the edge of the escarpment, the trail becomes more level and even and I'm comfortable stepping out to the brink.

All along the Ontario Escarpment I've been conscious of Douglas Larson's efforts to record the ages of white cedars in "the Ancient Cliff-Face Forest of the Niagara Escarpment." The oldest ones he found were further north, but in *The Last Stand* he and Peter Kelley picture a 597-year-old cedar on Rattlesnake Point named the Hunchback, and one 291 years old from Crawford Lake, the Cliff Giant. At Mount Nemo they located an 874-year-old cedar, the Amputee. I don't attempt to locate these trees—and the authors won't make them tourist sites even for rock climbers who might visit their cliff faces—but I seldom step close to a cedar with its toes hanging over the edge without wondering how long it has been growing there and what older trees might be below on the cliff face.

At the Escarpment Trail lookout point I scour the outlier across from me, hoping to see the cliffs below Rattlesnake Point. Eventually, I see a white rectangle in the midst of the dark trees, above deciduous trees of the canyon. It seems a very long way off, but I insist to myself that I have indeed stood above it.

* * *

Conservation Halton is the "neighbourhood conservation authority" of the Regional Municipality of Halton, near the shoreline of Lake Ontario southwest of Toronto and northwest of Hamilton. It maintains eight parks, including Crawford Lake, Rattlesnake Point, and Mount Nemo. The Mount Nemo Conservation Area is a day-use park, focused chiefly on hiking and climbing. A long walk up a gravel road to the Brock Harris Lookout ends at a large sign emphasizing "one of the best examples of a cliff-edge ecosystem in Ontario."

The view from the lookout, 295 meters (968 feet) above sea level—a diagram compares it to Toronto's CN Tower, another 300 meters higher—ranges over some 50 kilometers (31 miles). On the distant horizon, that sign claims, one might locate the outline of the Crawford Lake scarp, Nassagaweya Canyon, and Rattlesnake Point, as well as Toronto's skyscrapers and CN Tower. I try to create a multi-image panorama on my cellphone that captures escarpment sites as well as city ones.

Two loop trails diverge from the road to the lookout, each adjoined to the Bruce Trail. The map recommends trying "some of the many rock-climbing routes, both traditional and sport." The Amputee, that 884-years-old cedar clinging to the cliff face, might be spotted by climbers. The scarp also has caves, "important for bat nesting and hibernation." I wander a little way on both loop trails, peering over the precipice at the sheer cliff face and appreciating both the tenacity of the cedars and the height of the bluffs.

Conservation Halton asserts that "the seeds of the Niagara Escarpment Plan were sown" in Halton, following efforts to acquire 88 acres around Mount Nemo to prevent quarry expansion nearby. A more ambitious effort followed in 1985, and in 1990 UNESCO designated it as a World Biosphere Reserve. The sign points out that Walkers Line, the road below the escarpment, stretches "through the still rural landscape of the Halton watershed" but as it moves further east "increasing urbanization emphasizes the importance of protecting the Niagara Escarpment." Traffic grew heavier as I traveled south from Grey County through Dufferin County into the Halton Region, and metropolitan Toronto is barely an hour's drive away. For those who travel provincial thoroughfares past Rattlesnake Point or Mount Nemo, the scarps they can't avoid seeing are almost anomalies, a flashing glimpse of an escarpment unlikely to often be in their consciousness. Farther north, the abundance of woodland and vistas is a more constant reminder of the world that the province has settled on, a reminder that doesn't endure when the traveler is swallowed by the metropolis.

I leave the heights of Mount Nemo and circle around to Walkers Line for a more leisurely view of the scarp than I'd had coming down from the north. The road keeps me at a distance from the cliff face but at roughly 85 meters or 279 feet, the escarpment is easy to see as it bows out in my direction. Trees are thick along the top of the escarpment, tall along the talus base, but the cliffs are too high to camouflage. Many of the crevices seem deep and in the heights cedars cling and rise.

In a sense Mount Nemo is a good choice to stand in for the representative Niagara Escarpment scarp—the poster scarp, if you will, so accessible and so close to a large population that needs to identify more with the geologic formation that runs so persistently through the Great Lakes states and province. It would make an inviting introduction to the Escarpment for those unfamiliar with it. But (even as I write this) my mind races back to other scarps and the plains below them, the canyons that run through them, the forests above them and below them, the abundance of formations and structures and terrains that stretch back up the Bruce Peninsula and across Michigan and down through Wisconsin. What I would want would be for the introduction here to send hikers who encounter Mount Nemo venturing ever further north along the Bruce Trail, ever deeper into the cuesta, becoming ever more immersed in the escarpment. I would want them to travel on until they felt the Escarpment more fully within themselves.

21

The City of Hamilton cradles the west end of Lake Ontario and sprawls along its southern shore. A sandbar separates Lake Ontario from Hamilton Harbour. The deeper and narrower the harbour stretches west, the more it is surrounded by the Escarpment, which arcs around its end and adds an emphasis on terrain that the urbanized portion of the city to the east obscures. The city occupies two levels of landscape. Near the lake it sprawls across a wide strip of lake plain. Farther inland it rises onto the Niagara Cuesta, locally termed "the Mountain," 150 meters (492 feet) high.

The Niagara Peninsula between Lakes Ontario and Erie is between thirty and forty miles wide; its northern shoreline, from Hamilton to the Lewiston-Queenston Bridge, is a little over forty miles long and its southern shoreline nearly twice as long. When traveling from Michigan to New York, my wife and I crossed Ontario from Sarnia to Queenston, nearly 300 km (186 miles) in almost three hours; only near Hamilton would we notice the Escarpment before we drove the lake plain to the Niagara River.

Tracing the arc of the Escarpment due east, I'll pass through its most urban section, where the industrial, commercial, and cultural accumulation of the past obscures the terrain on which it all was constructed. Geological sites are listed under two conservation authorities: Hamilton, with a dozen conservation areas and a dozen more passive natural areas (with few or no facilities), and the Niagara Peninsula Conservation Authority, with over two dozen conservation areas east and south of Hamilton. Some will enrich my knowledge of the Escarpment.

* * *

The Spencer Gorge/Webster Falls Conservation Area northwest of Hamilton Harbour centers on a Y-shaped canyon formed by two remnants of glacial spillways, each with a significant waterfall— Webster Falls on Spencer Creek and Tew Falls on Logie's Creek.

Tew Falls, on the east side of the gorge, may have once been as large as Horseshoe Falls, the Canadian portion of Niagara Falls. Its height is 41 meters (134.5 feet), the tallest of Hamilton's waterfalls. It's a plunge waterfall, dropping directly from an overhang away from its recessed wall, and also a ribbon waterfall with a narrow flow.

Its closest lookout offers a clear view of the escarpment face. Foliage hangs off the edge, and ferns and lichen anchor themselves only about halfway down. Slopes above the creek bed are thick with greenery until trees from the bottom hide upper levels and blend in with trees along the scarp edge. Logie's Creek disappears from sight. A large flat stone sheet lies at an angle in the shallow plunge pool, sign of an earlier collapse of the lip. The bowl-shaped walls around the falls hint at a more powerful flowage in the past and an uninterrupted post-glacial erosion of the gorge.

Webster Falls is Hamilton's widest waterfall, spanning 30 meters (98 feet) across its crest and plunging 22 meters (72 feet). Spencer Creek, joined by Logie's, winds a long way through western Hamilton and empties into the Royal Botanical Gardens Cootes Paradise Sanctuary, a large, river-mouth wetlands at the tip of the harbour. It is the largest of several streams flowing into the wetlands with water from tributaries. Somewhere on Escarpment walls above the sanctuary is an "ancient White Cedar" that germinated in 1601, two years before the death of Queen Elizabeth I.

The Webster Falls Park, with a wheelchair accessible lookout area, cobblestone bridges, and washrooms, is open and hospitable, the falls visible from either side of the creek. From the west, I note low steps of strata at the brink, the creek width, and varying intensities of the flow.

I cross the arching bridge upstream for a closer view. There is no access to the bottom of the gorge, said to be "full of rare and sensitive plants and trees, some hundreds of years of old." The gorge is more exposed from the east side, far wider than the creek bed or the falls, a testament to millennia of erosion. Massive blocks of dolostone are in the top layers and deep recesses in the softer lower. Vegetation grows profusely on the talus but only occasionally at random fractures and joints between layers.

The blocks at the top of the Webster Falls gorge have a density, a solidity, seemingly impervious to change, incapable both of once never having been and of eventually never being, though the talus strewn along those gorges confirms the likelihood of the latter. Hamilton claimed once to have a hundred waterfalls, but a good many in the central city fell victim to increases in population, commerce, and industry. There are ways to eliminate the results of hundreds of thousands of years of sedimentation and erosion, but it's always encouraging to find places, as here, that resist human forces against nature.

* * *

In Ontario, "Eramosa Karst" is a familiar term over a century old, referring to distinctive strata in the Amabel-Lockport formation along the Eramosa River in Guelph, a city about 40 miles north-northwest of Hamilton. The Eramosa Karst Conservation Area is perched on Hamilton's upper level. In 1998, discovery of a large hole in the ground led to awareness of the area's accessible karst features. Declared an Area of Natural and Scientific Interest, it became a conservation area in 2008, claiming to have "the largest number of unique karst features" in the province, sixteen in all, including soil pipes, sinkholes, sinking streams, and a cave 335 meters [208 feet] long. It's a distinctive site on the Niagara Cuesta.

The Karst Features Trail leads me to area highlights, all at or below ground level. In karst terrain the nature of the incursion into the underworld varies. A soil pipe is a simple round hole of uncertain depth; a sinkhole or doline can take on the appearance of a crater or quarry and collapse without warning (one near Tampa, Florida swallowed two houses and grew to 225 feet wide and 50 feet deep); underground streams can siphon off above ground streams, create tunnels and caves, and resurface as springs; openings in the roofs of caves will provide windows into them and views of subsurface streams running through them.

The Eramosa Karst Conservation Area makes me conscious of what lies beneath my feet. Standing on the top or at the base of a scarp, I concentrate on the vertical, on the height and sheerness of the precipice; standing on karst terrain, I'm aware of the horizontal, the active hidden layers and glimpses into their depths. Permanent though they seem, the Escarpment cliffs remind me of their impermanence by the talus at their feet. The terrain of the cuesta is impermanent too, not only by wearing away its scarp, but also by wearing away its interior, hinted at by sinks and exposed by dolines.

Completing the circuit, I stall a little, reminding myself that the Niagara Escarpment isn't simply a series of individual cliff faces and heights; it's also the cuesta those scarps front and that stretches behind them, the terrain from which those scarps are formed and that connects them all to one another. This Eramosa strata is present in the Amabel/Lockport Formation all the way north to Manitoulin Island and all the way east into western New York. I need to keep the scope of the cuesta in mind.

* * *

The Ball's Falls Conservation Area, a Niagara Peninsula Conservation Authority site, centers on Twenty Mile Creek, which winds north to empty into Lake Ontario. The building of a grist mill on the creek's east bank established a small community here and a cluster of restored historic buildings still stand near the Lower Falls: a family home, an operating flour mill, a church, a blacksmith shop, a lime kiln, and the like. The Upper Falls is about a mile upstream from the Lower on a forested trail along the western bank. The Ball's Falls Centre for Conservation features displays on the area's history, the Niagara Escarpment, and the watershed.

Strolling down from the Centre, I cross the bridge into the Lower Falls area where families wander among the buildings and a father and a few children are leaving the Lower Falls lookout. The Lower Falls is 27 meters (88 feet) high and, because its height and width are nearly equal, the Conservation Area terms it "a classic waterfall." A sign emphasizes how Ball's Falls' "geologic formations are exposed to reveal the geologic history" and directs attention to visible rock layers dating back nearly 438 million years, "common to the entire Niagara Escarpment, from Queenston to Tobermory, Ontario." A diagram displays Escarpment levels revealed here, from the Lockport Dolostone, Rochester Shale, and Irondequoit Limestone of the Upper Falls to the strata of the Lower Falls and beyond, illustrating what erosion has removed to form the gorge running to the Lake Ontario shoreline. An illustration shows the differences in the gorges of the Lower Falls and the Upper Falls, the location of a former riverbed and gorges gouged out, filled in, and abandoned, and areas of steep slopes and escarpment levels.

I backtrack to the bridge to take the Cataract Trail, a dirt path on the side of a slope, a little steep and rocky but mostly undemanding. It weaves around rocks and boulders and past outcrops of mossy strata among the trees. Exposed escarpment perches over high slopes of overgrown talus. The village noises fade and sounds of the Upper Falls grow louder. Beyond the remnant ruins of a woolen mill, I reach the lookout.

The Upper Falls is a curtain waterfall, its width greater than its height, which is 11 meters (36 feet). The greater height and power of the Lower Falls made it the site of the grist mill and the subsequent community around it, leaving the Upper Falls somewhat more isolated. Its natural setting is more dramatic than that of the Lower Falls. The creek bed above the falls is more uneven, with separate stone plates breaking up the flow. At midstream the creek divides into two streams plummeting over the edge. On the opposite side, poised in a corner, is a large box-shaped piece of dolostone, likely a section of the grey-brown caprock of the Lockport Formation. The diagram that shows the vanished part of the gorge labels one short section as "Karst" and I wonder if Eramosa karst is exposed in the gorge wall.

Across from the lookout, water streams out of the eastern wall in several places. Each stream is considerably lighter than the water channeled over the falls, but the creek is not flowing so strongly that it has somehow overflowed its banks and added to the width of the falls, almost making it a horseshoe shape. A closer look at that eastern wall confirms that the water is flowing not over the wall but from within it. The scarp there rises considerably higher than the creek bed above the falls, and at its base, lining its plunge pool, are large flat blocks of talus that could only have come from above. I wonder about the karst composition of the upper levels of the gorge. The Upper Falls is roughly on the same elevation of the "Mountain" that the Eramosa Karst Conservation Area is.

The foaming white water drops behind the talus along the east wall into the deep brown waters of the plunge pool and disappears into a light chocolate creek. Recalling the falls at the other end of the Mountain I ponder the landscape that connects them. I'd driven here on heavily trafficked streets and highways, past homes and businesses and bustling construction. My imagination strained to lift the urban and suburban and semi-rural buildings and roads off that terrain, return it to something like the woods at Ball's Falls, the open meadows of Eramosa Karst, and the forest and slopes of Spencer Gorge. I tried to imagine the fields and woods of an undeveloped cuesta looking off from its heights over an undeveloped lake plain. I didn't have much luck.

* * *

Eastbound for the Niagara River, I stop at the St. Catherine's Museum and Welland Canal Centre for a quick look at the Welland Canal, the passage through the Niagara Peninsula between Lakes Ontario and Erie that allows vessels to bypass the river. I'll visit the Erie Canal in New York soon and want to know the difference between them. The museum's model of the Escarpment at the east end of the peninsula puts Niagara Falls, the lakes, the canal, and the shift between scarp and lake plain all in perspective.

The model faces south from Lake Ontario, Lake Erie in the background beyond the land. The Escarpment snakes above the Ontario plain and the Canal winds down the center of the model. To the east the Niagara Gorge is deep and wide, and the canyon obscures the river flowing through the escarpment. On the cuesta or on a map, the canal seems mostly level and straightforward, but the model reminds you that the locks have to lift vessels up or down the escarpment, a rather tremendous task.

I push on toward Queenston Heights. In the past, growing up in Lockport and later teaching in the Ontario lakeshore town of Wilson, I often crossed into Canada. With friends I went to stock car races in Thorold or took in Niagara Falls; I saw plays at the Shaw Festival in Niagara-on-the-Lake and toured the Fort George Historic Site, to compare it to Fort Niagara across the river. I feel myself on familiar terrain.

The Niagara Peninsula ends at the Niagara River and the Niagara Escarpment in Ontario ends at Queenston Heights National Historic Site. The most prominent feature there is the Brock Monument, commemorating the death of Major General Sir Isaac Brock at the battle of Queenston Heights in 1812, when British and Canadian forces repelled an attempted invasion by American forces. Brock's grave is in the base of a 190-foot classical column, an ornate and impressive monument, its viewing deck offering a grand vista.

Below Queenston Heights to the north, the Lake Ontario Plain spreads out to Niagara-on-the-Lake and the mouth of the Niagara River. To the east across the river is the village of Lewiston. A bridge connects Queenston and Lewiston, and both communities take pride in being located at the place on the Escarpment where the Niagara Falls began.

Though Lake Ontario is still too far away to see, gazing at the Niagara River offers a sense of where it is headed. It also offers a sense of where the Niagara Escarpment is headed, a continuation of the heights that have angled through the Niagara Peninsula its entire length. To follow those heights, of course, it will be necessary to cross the gorge the Niagara River has been carving for some 12,000 years, the gorge the Niagara Falls are still working on.

The Gorge

The Niagara River forms the eastern border of Ontario's Niagara Peninsula and the western border of New York's Niagara Frontier. It empties Lake Erie and, through it, Lakes Superior, Michigan, Huron, and St. Clair, into Lake Ontario. The gap in the Niagara Escarpment between Queenston, Ontario and Lewiston, New York is where the river began carving a gorge seven miles upstream to where it now plummets over the escarpment between Niagara Falls, Ontario and Niagara Falls, New York. It's the point for which the Niagara Escarpment was named, though the geologic formation itself runs a thousand miles through three states and one province. The Niagara Cuesta on either side of the river slopes south toward Lake Erie in Ontario and toward the parallel Onondaga Escarpment in New York. The Niagara River, its falls, and its gorge are essential and elemental, powerful to behold and profound to experience; it's all most visitors know about the Niagara Escarpment. The terrain beyond that riverine corridor is essentially *terra incognita.*

I grew up some twenty miles east of the Niagara River, in a city on the Escarpment. I walked some of its trails, approached the falls on the Maid of the Mist, stood behind the falls in the Cave of the Winds, gazed at the American Falls when its water had been diverted and the riverbed was dry, sailed with a friend near the river's mouth, stood with my wife almost alone above the falls in wind and swirling snow on a frigid New Year's Eve. In all those random visits I never fully grasped what I was seeing.

I've come to the Gorge intent on finally discovering it.

* * *

Silurian sediments in the Niagara Gorge date back between 430 and 415 million years; about 12,300 years ago the recession of the Wisconsin ice sheet created Glacial Lake Iroquois, a higher, broader precursor to Lake Ontario, and a larger version of Lake Erie that drained into a huge glacial lake, Lake Tonawanda, perched between the Niagara and Onondaga Escarpments. Several spillways flowed from Lake Tonawanda into Lake Iroquois, but as the land rebounded from the glaciers, the Niagara River spillway became the primary drainage point. Roughly 11,000 years ago the Niagara River plummeted into a plunge pool between Lewiston and Queenston, the first site of Niagara Falls, and began steadily carving through the cuesta.

Across centuries Native Americans viewed the falls at various locations. Samuel de Champlain mentioned them in 1604, though he never saw them. The missionary Father Louis Hennepin, traveling with LaSalle, saw them in 1678. He claimed, "They plunge down a height of more than five hundred feet," and their "waters foam and boil in a fearful manner. [...] the noise which they make is heard for more than fifteen leagues." Hennepin's distorted but spectacular drawing of the Falls shows a man with his hands covering his ears. The Jesuit writer Charlevoix later described the western falls as a horseshoe and judged the height more accurately at 140–150 feet. After the War of 1812, the Niagara Frontier opened up to extensive settlement and tourism. Basil Hall, Fanny Trollope, Alexis de Tocqueville, Harriet Martineau,

Nathaniel Hawthorne, Charles Dickens, Fredrika Bremer, George William Curtis, and Anthony Trollope all wrote travel accounts still worth reading.

The travel piece resonating most with me is "Sketches of Scenery on the Niagara River," written by the painter Louisa Davis Minot in July 1815 and published in *The North American Review*. Katherine Manthorne calls Minot's two paintings of Niagara Falls "impressive" and "accomplished" but argues, "The terrible beauty of the waterfall comes across in her writing just as effectively as in her painting."

Minot's article highlights the falls' power and beauty and describes the devastation still apparent in the aftermath of battles along the river. She doesn't simply observe the river and the falls but reacts to them as fully as she can, while feeling the scope of warfare's local impact. Her sense of immediacy and parallel attention to natural setting and cultural setting sets the stage for much writing about Niagara Falls that will follow.

Travelers come to Niagara Falls to view their scale and consider their power, but in the two centuries since Minot visited them, forces of commerce and industry created a new world around them, most flagrantly centered on entertainment and recreation—fireworks and lightshows, wax museums and amusement halls, boat rides to the falls and aerocars and ziplines above the gorge; physically intrusive aspects of excavating, boring, and diverting the river's flow to generate electricity, power industry, even reshape it for the convenience of tourists. Ginger Strand's often acerbic *Inventing Niagara: Beauty, Power, and Lies* details a history of exploitation and renovation. Tightrope walkers no longer cross the gorge and daredevils no longer go over the falls in barrels, but people come to Niagara Falls for entertainment and recreation with only cursory attention to the geological formation that inspired centuries of tourism. Elsewhere on the Escarpment, we witness how a waterfall provokes an entrepreneur to build a mill and the mill encourages a community and more industry and settlement follow, until, over time, the community turns to fresh enterprises. The difference at Niagara Falls lies chiefly in the scale.

Louisa Minot helps us understand the effect of the Falls on the sensibility of someone visiting it before commercial development of its sight-seeing potential or its industrial utility. Now I come with a different perspective than I had in the past, hoping to connect to Escarpment and Cuesta here and fit the Falls into their Arc.

22

In "Sketches of Scenery on the Niagara River" Louisa Davis Minot travels north from Lake Erie, the year after a devastating battle was fought at Fort Erie. She writes that the American visitor will "examine the trees that are shattered, and the ground that has been torn up by the balls and rockets" and "water the roses that are already growing on the soldier's grave." But eventually, she imagines, "this ruin will be indiscriminately mingled with the soil," the "storm will have levelled these sandy graves, with the beach, on which they are thrown up" and travelers will "seek in vain for those vestiges of war, either on the face of the country, or in the hearts of its inhabitants." Today, except for Brock's Monument on Queenston Heights, little along either side of the Niagara River recalls the War of 1812.

After Fort Erie, Minot mainly focuses on the river, writing that the "bed of the river descends gradually," its current "gentle" and "tranquil," but nearer the falls, "the scene changes. The roar deepens, the spray rises a lofty column of vapour in the heavens, the *rapids*, which commence about a mile above the brink of the Falls, now shew their white heads, and the current increases its force." The Dufferin Islands Natural Area, just south of the Falls where the rapids begin, is a remnant of a wider Niagara River. Glacial deposits still perch on the Lockport dolostone of the riverbed but rapids have scoured glacial debris off the bedrock. A diagram in *Colossal Cataract: The Geologic History of Niagara Falls* marks the falls' locations across millennia—at the lip of the escarpment between Queenston and Lewiston 12,000 years ago; further upstream 4,000 and 2,000 years ago; in 1678, when Hennepin saw them; and now. The scale of erosion is impressive in the relatively short distance Horseshoe Falls has receded in the last three and a half centuries. Had the river flowed at its usual rate, it would have reached Dufferin Islands by 2500 CE.

North of Dufferin Islands, a lookout point highlights the rusted hull of a dumping scow stranded mid-river. A hundred years ago it broke loose from a tug and floated toward the falls, until someone aboard grounded it in the shallows. The man's resourcefulness saved him from either riding it over the falls or attempting to swim the rapids—he was hauled to shore in a breeches buoy. The scow remains in the rapids, a reminder of the limits where vessels must not go.

The Horseshoe Rapids lie between the crest of Horseshoe Falls and a control structure regulating the river's flow, channeling part into hydroelectrical facilities, part toward the falls. The amount going over the falls varies daily, a larger amount in daylight hours with tourists watching, a lesser amount overnight. The Rapids are turbulent any time of day.

At the crest of the Horseshoe Falls, I remember Frederic Church's 1857 40 x 90½ inch painting, "Niagara." A couple of houses and a stone tower are visible in the background, but Church has so emphasized the torrents pouring over the falls and the turbulence all through the horseshoe that human presence is insignificant, even irrelevant. And so it proves on site. Shadowy shapes indicate commercial structures along the eastern shoreline. Church shows no islands, only small rocky shapes with sparse foliage indicate the rough surface

of the riverbed over which the current tumbles. The roar of the falls overwhelms any other sounds around me.

Louisa Davis Minot haunts me again at the wide, open area of Table Rock, extending along the gorge. One of her paintings portrays Horseshoe Falls from a much lower perspective than Church chose forty years later. Minot accessed Table Rock down a steep hill and across a marsh and "through brushwood amidst lofty trees" rather than, as I did, past parking areas, a food court, gift shops, a restaurant, and paved walkways. A traveler then could descend, with difficulty, to a point below Table Rock, which she described as "a deep cavern, between the sheet of water and the rock," and experience "a storm that is continually generating and bursting, [...] confounding every sense [...] with darkness and noise and motion." One of her paintings takes that perspective.

Table Rock was then a promontory that Minot described as "a single stratum of lime stone, about a foot thick; projecting several yards beyond the perpendicular precipice, and hanging over the gulf below." She noted how exposed and intimate the connection between the traveler and the river might be. "Here you may sit on the edge, with your feet over the chasm, and dip your hand in the torrent as it rushes over the brink," she writes. "You fancy that the rock losing its slight hold, is sliding with you, down the precipice. You believe that you could sail on those clouds of vapour which are rolling around, and are almost tempted to make the experiment." In fact, bit by bit, Table Rock was losing its slight hold, part of it falling in 1818. Other parts later collapsed from time to time—in 1850, an empty carriage toppled with it. The remaining overhang was blasted away in 1935 and Table Rock became simply a flat area above the gorge.

Overlooking the falls, Louisa Minot noted that "prismatick colours are reflected from the spray, in different positions, varying as the sun advances in his course." The rainbow "spans the whole scene" mornings and evenings, and at noon seemingly "floats on the surface below." In the present day, late in the evening, hundreds of colored LED lights illuminate the falls at a magnitude more brilliant than nature's mere rainbows.

* * *

The Journey Behind the Falls elevator descends 150 feet to tunnels bored into dolostone that allow visitors to stand behind Horseshoe Falls and watch seven million gallons of water fall at 40 miles an hour each second. Inside the Escarpment two nearly square portals, eerily lit within, face the falls. Water swirls along the floor of the short passage between the opening and the slightly raised fenced walkway; in one portal, a slab of fallen rock perches at the edge. A third opening leads onto a sheltered observation deck for a view of the falls and the gorge wall. Mist obscures the recessed space behind the current. Across the horseshoe, the bottom of the falls is veiled in clouds of mist, but a sightseeing Maid of the Mist rocks there, ponchoed figures lining its top deck. To the east, the escarpment stretches below Goat Island to the long white cloud at the base of the American Falls. The river gorge seems foggy into the distance.

The observation deck is anchored midway down the steep talus slope on Horseshoe Falls' west side, lush green coating rocks from the Escarpment's bottom to the water's edge. The scarp leans forward. Blocks of stone scattered thickly near its base are reminders of the river's persistent recession. Standing in the spray of the torrent, watching the river plunge over Horseshoe Falls, overwhelmed by its roar, we seem small and impermanent, less significant than talus.

* * *

The magisterial gaze. The words "Niagara Falls" likely bring such a commanding perspective to mind, sweeping across the American, Bridal Veil, and Horseshoe Falls. Passengers gain it entering Hornblower Niagara Cruises, slowly making their way from the brink of the gorge to the dock at river's edge and gazing at distant steam rising from the Horseshoe Falls, mists churning at the base of the American Falls, and tour boats making their circuit.

Decades ago, after my wife and I rode the Maid of the Mist, the impression it made stayed with me. The Hornblower and Maid of the Mist vessels pass one another, one departing the roiling waters of Horseshoe Falls and the other approaching, red plastic ponchos on Canadian passengers and yellow ponchos on American passengers fluttering before the white of the falls. Poncho-clad tourists clamber around hazy paths in the talus on either side of each falls. Walking down to the dock gives us a closer view of the gorge wall the Queen Victoria Park Shelter perches upon. Intermittently, people glide down a 2,200-foot long zipline at 40 miles an hour from a starting height of 220 feet. It makes a memorable Go-Pro home video, but its connection to the setting seems dubious, a safe equivalent of tightrope walking above the falls or plummeting over them in a barrel.

The passengers are regimented into boarding lines. One boat departs, another comes in, and a throng mingles on an outbound vessel's foredeck. At river level, rising mist sometimes hides the bottom of the falls almost entirely and, as the boat draws nearer, it seems to enter a cloud. When it thins, huge blocks of talus extending into the river appear at the bases of the American Falls, the narrower Bridal Veil Falls, and Luna Island, the scarp-edge island between them. On the top of the scarp, another line of tourists approaches the crest of the falls, and blue ponchoed people leave the bottom of the Observation Tower to climb toward the edge of the American Falls. Below Goat Island, yellow ponchoed figures move along wooden walkways on their Cave of the Winds tour. A scattering of gulls perched on shrubs below exposed escarpment watch them pass.

Almost everyone around me has a cellphone or computer tablet and everyone, at the railing or in spaces further back, holds them up for photos. Images of other people's iPhones and iPads will crowd my own photographs. It's difficult to recapture the frame of mind I entered on my first approach to the bottom of the falls, something like overwhelming awe at their mass and power and volume and a sense of the frailty and insignificance of the man-made object that carried me there. I try to concentrate on the falls but instead glance around me at the wet, dripping, staring faces and acknowledge their smiles, their delight in the cold mist, their unsteady footing on the rocking vessel, the effort to take in the scale of what they face. I turn back to the falls to see and feel for myself what they see and feel. The invigorating cold spray of the mist, the relentless roar of the torrent. I notice someone recording the sound—any number are taking videos, but she wants only the sound, perhaps to listen to with her eyes closed in the night, reliving the moment as if it were solitary and personal.

* * *

It's a long way from the escarpment edge over which Horseshoe Falls plummets to the escarpment edge where the Gorge began. The distance is a thick volume of geological history, recording changes in river levels and riverbeds and shorelines and channels. The Escarpment and its cuesta display more than torrential spectacle. No longer overwhelmed by the falls' tumult, it's possible to concentrate on the gorge's exposed walls, take in the heights from which the riverbed was worn away, observe the strata that the river gouged its way through, study stretches of smooth flowing water and stretches of tumbling, turbulent rapids.

The top of the gorge is sometimes open, cultivated parkland; more often it is tree-lined, with buildings peeking through. Trees and bushes often climb halfway up the wall from talus at the river's edge. In some stretches, the current hews close to the wall and in others stays at the edge of lowlands. The exposed rock wall makes clear the variety in the layers of strata, at the highest the thick solid block of Lockport dolostone, below it thinner layers and changes in composition. Huge boulders, broken from above, rest at the very river's edge. The river, compressed into a narrower space than it was upstream or than it will be when it reaches the Ontario Plain, foams and plunges.

Where the gorge breaks open on its western bank, the river turns sharply and its waters churn in a whirlpool. The Whirlpool Aero Car glides above it on steel cables, from south to north and back. Sometimes the Whirlpool Jet Boat streaks upriver into the Whirlpool and then beyond into the rapids, and quiet passengers on the aero car hear jet boat passengers squeal. The whirlpool resulted from the intersection of the river with the pre-glacial St. David's Gorge, dating back some 22,800 years, which the receding Wisconsin Ice Sheet buried in outwash. Carving its way upstream on a separate route 12,000 years ago, the Niagara River eventually reached St. David's Gorge, washed out its silt, and formed the Whirlpool. Observers above the Whirlpool are not simply in the presence of aero cars, jet boats, and swirling waters, but in the presence of geologic history older than the last ice age.

North of the Whirlpool, and challengingly accessible from it on foot, the Niagara Glen Nature Reserve changes the dimensions of the Niagara River Gorge. Wintergreen Flats, a small park east of Niagara Parkway, offers an overview of the gorge and a sprawling wooded area on the riverbank. The broader Niagara River of around 10,500 years ago carved a wider gorge here, until water levels dropped and its channel narrowed. The Nature Reserve is essentially an abandoned portion of that wider riverbed and now has trails winding through it, reachable by a long descent along the cliff face.

The trails here pass in stages through and beyond isolated sections of rock, sometimes narrow passages, sometimes formations like a balanced rock or an arch or a large pothole.

It's possible to locate fossil trilobites, extinct for 250 million years. At the lowest level, a path winds above the current channel and overlooks an eddy at the broadest part. The paths are winding and rocky, but the reserve seems so isolated that the hiker gains a sense of timelessness, a feeling of being closer to the geologic history of the gorge than upstream overlooks and tours can provide.

Beyond Niagara Glen and past pleasant tourist stops—the Butterfly Conservatory, the Floral Clock—and proof of the river's profitable power in the Sir Adam Beck Hydroelectric Station Reservoir, I reach the Queenston Heights Park. At Queenston Heights both cultural history and natural history are commemorated.

The impressive, stalwart Brock Monument honors Major-General Isaac Brock, the British commander-in-chief who died at the battle of Queenston Heights; nearby is the Laura Secord Homestead, honoring the woman who warned the British of an impending American invasion. When Louisa Minot toured the Niagara River, the War of 1812 was fresh in memory and, but for the monument and the homestead, the visitor will, as she predicted, "seek in vain for those vestiges of war." Nearby is the Bruce Trail Southern Terminus Cairn, closing the link to the cairn at Tobermory. A bilingual plaque erected by the Ontario Heritage Foundation proclaims that *"Queenston Heights fait partie de l'escarpement du Niagara, relief qui traverse l'Ontario sur 725 kilometers des chutes du Niagara à l'île Mantoulin."* The plaque explains the Escarpment's composition and terrain and its 1990 designation by the United Nations as a World Biosphere Reserve.

From Queenston Heights the view across the river faces the continuation of the escarpment at Lewiston, New York.

Here, below the escarpment, the river widens as it winds across the Ontario Plain toward Lake Ontario, less than ten miles away. At the mouth of the river, Fort Niagara State Park on the American shore and Fort George National Historic Site on the Canadian offer well-maintained reminders of military history and, on a clear day, hints of metropolitan Toronto across the lake. For the geologically minded, the Ontario Plain and the Niagara Escarpment confirm varying lake levels over past millennia, and the view from Queenston Heights invites quiet contemplation of the long arc of natural history.

23

Goat Island, on the American side of the Gorge, divides the river, 90% of the water flowing toward Horseshoe Falls, 10% toward the Bridal Veil and American Falls. Footbridges on its south side connect to the small, forested Three Sisters Islands at the edge of rapids extending across to the Dufferin Islands. The island is close to the rapids' most turbulent sections where low steps in the uneven riverbed make the river foam and writhe.

Smaller islands ring Goat Island, some essentially boulders, larger ones well wooded. The rapids around islands in the channel between Goat Island and the mainland is nowhere as daunting as those above Horseshoe Falls. Some islands are surmounted with gravels and silt 35 feet higher than the dolostone-capped falls.

Goat Island offers proximity to the falls. In Ontario, you view the falls across the gorge from the western edge of Horseshoe Falls; on Goat Island, you reach the northeast edge of Horseshoe Falls, the northern edge of Bridal Veil Falls, and the southern edge of the American Falls. Terrapin Point, the Horseshoe Falls overlook, was once part of the upper riverbed, but after river water levels were controlled and the bed dried there, it was developed into an observation site. From here, mist hides the opposite side of the Horseshoe, only the talus below the east side and jagged edges of the rocky banks showing where water passes.

At the center of Goat Island, the Cave of the Winds tour takes travelers down to the Hurricane Deck, an intricate series of stairs and walkways across talus to within twenty feet of the "billowing torrents" of Bridal Veil Falls, where they consider the exposed dolostone bluff on which Goat Island and Luna Island both perch. Tourists in plastic ponchos and special footwear stand out against the red bridges and fences of the deck. The tour once allowed passage behind the falls but the overhanging ledge was judged to be unstable and blasted away in 1955. Near the tour office, a monument to Nikola Tesla, who designed the first hydroelectric power plant in Niagara Falls, stands quietly on the path.

From Goat Island, I descend to a viewing plaza on small Luna Island at the escarpment edge. Larger islands extend back from Luna Island, increasing and narrowing the length of the Bridal Veil channel. Bridal Veil Falls is an arm of American Falls, separated from it by Luna Island. Across the river, the Canadian side of the gorge spreads out panoramically, the escarpment wall lined with a green-clad talus slope along the river, layers of stone above it, buildings offering viewpoints and river adventures above them, and structures higher than the falls towering across the skyline—the Skylon Tower, the Niagara Skywheel, a hotel or casino. From the Bridal Veil overlook, the west side of Horseshoe Falls is momentarily unobscured by mist.

I cross to the edge of the American Falls. From the Ontario shore the full width of American Falls seems fairly straight-edged, but from Luna Island on the New York shore its rim looks jagged and uneven, even "saw-toothed." At one point the falls are so indented that another horseshoe seems to be forming. Uneven piles of talus filling the plunge pool testify to constant erosion. It is assumed that the American Falls will never be able to wear away that talus, perched on a shelf of resistant Irondequoit limestone extending into the river.

A walkway from Goat Island leads across a bridge to Green Island, the largest island in the American Falls channel, and then to a second bridge linking to the mainland and more tourist sites, the Maid of the Mist tour and the Observation Tower where tourists descend to the base of the falls and climb to the Crow's Nest, a viewing platform facing the crest. Walking along the rapids towards Prospect Point I'm conscious of the turbulence of the water, the rocky undersurface, the way the water dips and surges and splashes and curls back on itself as it crosses underwater dips or rises or obstructions. At the lip of the American Falls denuded tree limbs and a candelabra-like section of multiple branches bounce through the rapids to slide over the edge.

Prospect Point is a lookout area on the north bank of American Falls. The falls foam and spray and sometimes the mist is so thick it's impossible to see as far as Horseshoe Falls or even Luna Island. Geologists theorize that the recession of Horseshoe Falls will one day intercept the channel that carries the river to the American Falls and cut the current off, leaving it and the Bridal Veil Falls dry, their riverbed simply a lower extension of the bluffs below Goat Island and Prospect Point. In 1969 the U.S. Army Corps of Engineers diverted water from the American Falls to conduct a six-month long geological survey, ostensibly searching for "instabilities" and studying "structural integrity." A temporary walkway allowed tourists out onto the riverbed and wild and domestic animals plundered formerly islanded bird nests. Those of us witnessing that diversion decades ago know what that riverbed will look like. Standing here now, it's hard to imagine the falls drying up; even in its reduced flow, determined by hydroelectric diversions, the American Falls exhibits a magnitude that seems permanent, unstoppable.

* * *

Over a forty-year period, the Great Gorge Route trolley carried visitors downstream along the American side, over a bridge between Lewiston and Queenston, and back upstream along the Canadian side. After the International Railway Company lost access to Ontario, it operated the New York portion until 1935, when 5,000 tons of falling rock destroyed part of the railbed. The rails were soon removed, but route sections still exist. The Great Gorge Railway Trail is one of several current trails along the New York side of the river, running for little over a mile from the Niagara Falls Discovery Center to an intersection with the Niagara Gorge Rim Trail. That 6.2-mile trail links Terrapin Point's view of Horseshoe Falls with Artpark State Park in Lewiston, at the escarpment edge where the gorge began.

Views across the river from the trail are expansive. Exposed rock strata above the thick growth of trees on the talus is stark and cragged, and an occasional cave appears midway up the wall. Trees along the top disguise buildings behind them. Upstream towards the Rainbow Bridge and distant clouds of mist at the falls, the skyline of Niagara Falls, Ontario is clear and prominent; downstream toward the Whirlpool Bridge, only a distant hotel rises above the New York tree line. Sometimes abandoned riverside structures can be seen below sheer walls. At a flat gravel overlook with a low protective wall arching around it, three women photograph seven or eight children on the other side of the wall, the kids either pretending to have climbed up the side of the gorge or to be about to plummet down it. The exposed ground beyond the wall is not so wide that I share the women's amused delight in their rambunctious children.

The trail descends gradually and sinks below the level of the rim, the rock wall higher to the east, trees to the west obscuring views of the gorge. Starkly exposed rock layers rising above the trail vary in thickness and color and roughness. Signs along the trail encourage visitors to spend time identifying different compositions here. One labels a group of blocky rock layers as Dolostone, forming the crest of the falls, and another names different stones as Grimsby Sandstone, pointing out their red color. Remembering the gorge wall alongside the Horseshoe Falls, I appreciate the dryness and quiet here.

The Niagara Gorge Rim Trail eventually passes through Whirlpool State Park and Devil's Hole State Park on the way to the Niagara Escarpment at Artpark. I turn back. At the overlook where I saw the women and children, I'm relieved to find them gone.

* * *

At Whirlpool State Park, scenic overlooks above the river provide perspective on the Whirlpool and the Aero Car transit above it. Stairs lead down to where rocks line the rapids, exposed when water levels dropped and the river carved itself lower.

The Niagara Scenic Parkway Trail at river level leads upstream past the Whirlpool along the Whirlpool Rapids where hikers can step out onto the Whirlpool Sandstone. Downstream, the trail goes past Devil's Hole Rapids to Devil's Hole State Park where another staircase connects to the Niagara Gorge Rim Trail, linking back to Whirlpool State Park. Hikers taking that two-and-a-half-mile loop spend half their hike on the edge of the river, making a significant descent at one end and a significant ascent at the other.

Devil's Hole is a notch in the gorge wall, a re-entrant formed when Lake Tonawanda, the post-glacial body of water between the Niagara Escarpment and the Onondaga Escarpment, drained here and created its own gorge. Several north-flowing spillways linked Lake Tonawanda to Glacial Lake Ontario, each eventually closed off by changing water levels until only the spillway between what is now Queenston and Lewiston drained Lake Tonawanda. At that point the Niagara Falls began.

Past the Devil's Hole a stone staircase descends to a trail winding down to the river and onto that trail along the rapids. The descent starts at the top of the gorge and continues along the Escarpment wall as it goes lower. It's easy to stay attuned to the textures of the strata. The top layer is thick and heavy Lockport Dolostone that serves as the edge of the falls, and succeeding layers are often thin and jagged, until DeCew Dolostone emerges, another thick layer. The unevenness of the  strata, the way the top layer juts out past the supporting layers, the way the lower layers return to the bulk of the upmost layer, all suggest the incremental deposition of various sediments over the Silurian era. The Devil's Hole and the gorge wall are distant from the river, indicating the great width and volume of the river's erosive power in the past. Succeeding levels of the trail display stone worn away at different times, some startlingly fractured and jointed. The Devil's Hole descent offers a layer-by-layer indication of the length of time it took to form the gorge.

Ginger Strand, in *Inventing Niagara*, called Devil's Hole "an impressive spot, a semicircular natural amphitheater carved out of the gorge cliff in flaky striations" and claimed that if you "make your way down through the crisp scrub, the rocky face of Devil's Hole looming ever higher above you," you eventually get "to face the noise and fury" of the rapids. She found it stunning, in part because elsewhere she felt hard pressed to appreciate Niagara Falls as a natural wonder. That Niagara Falls, she wrote, "doesn't exist anymore. Manicured, repaired, landscaped and artificially lit, dangerous overhangs dynamited off and water flow managed to suit the tourist schedule, the Falls are more a monument to man's meddling than to nature's strength." As I follow the Niagara Escarpment, I try to stay aware of the gorge that the Niagara River has carved into the Niagara Cuesta and shut out the recreational and industrial aspects of the location as often as I can. As a nature hiker, I've been out of my element here, missing the chance to lose myself on remote—or at least semi-remote—trails in the woods.

Rather than visit the Niagara Power Project's Power Vista Visitor's Center and the Robert Moses Power Plant, to admire how the falls and the river have been harnessed to serve hydroelectric power, I drive into Lewiston, down the Escarpment and then back up it to the northern end of the Rim Trail in Artpark. With my wife and a brother-in-law,

I once walked the trail upstream from Artpark to beyond the Lewiston-Queenston Bridge, trying to imagine a trolley line running up the center of the trail.

I was somewhat familiar with the area. My father took me to an archaeological dig there, encouraging my interest in the field and, after an hour scraping dirt carefully with a spoon, ending my enthusiasm for it. Years later, after the state park was dedicated to former State Senator Earl W. Brydges (coincidentally the father of a student I once taught), that archaeological site—the Lewiston Mound, a Hopewell burial mound—was named to the National Register of Historic Places and Artpark was established as an artist residency and performance venue. For years, I routinely crossed the Lewiston-Queenston Bridge from our home in Michigan to visit family in Niagara County. Only on that walk with my wife and brother-in-law did I pay attention to the Niagara Gorge and start to have a sense of the Escarpment.

Across the river from the Niagara Gorge Rim Trail the Brock Monument rises through the trees above the gorge. The wall there is dense with trees climbing from the riverbank and towering over the top. It's possible to discern a narrow portion of cliff face and to realize how high glacial debris has been deposited. The stark bluffs so evident upstream, closer to the falls, are lower in the landscape here.

To the south, the international bridge stands high above the river, flags centered midway. To the north, the river widens making its way to Lake Ontario. The dark green river flowing through the forested gorge lightens as riverbanks lower and immense blue sky above the lake brightens the view.

Here is where the Niagara River began falling over the escarpment that would be named for the river, the starting point for the Niagara Falls so celebrated seven miles upstream. Here, in time, came the realization of geologists and geographers that the Escarpment stretched to the west a very great distance—New York-born Increase Lapham discerned its presence in Wisconsin almost two hundred years ago—as well as stretched to the east, across western New York State. Despite changes wrought by man, the Niagara Falls still inspire awe and admiration and divert attention from the Niagara Escarpment, its thousand-mile arc, and the cuesta sprawling across states and province.

But here where the Niagara Gorge began, I ready myself to return into the landscape where their existence determined mine.

New York

What sense of the Escarpment do travelers take with them after visiting Niagara Falls? Most central must be that panorama of plunging water, perhaps some awareness of exposed cataract walls and island bluffs. Those who took walking tours and boating adventures will recall the power of torrential waters, but it takes more determined venturing to visit the Rapids and the Whirlpool, Devil's Hole and Niagara Glen. These sites move the traveler's thoughts away from feelings of awe, majesty, and scale engendered by the falls.

And then they go home. Decades ago, in the middle of the night, I drove college friends to Niagara Falls. By daylight we reached the falls. After our return to college, we never spoke of the excursion again, an inconsequential weekend escapade. I had shared with my friends from eastern New York the most prominent aspect of my home ground in western New York—not where I really lived but what travelers for over a century felt was its most memorable element.

If I'd known more about my home ground, I wouldn't have identified myself with Niagara Falls. I would have known that, to get there, we crossed the cuesta the Niagara Escarpment fronts; that the town where we visited my slumbering parents and siblings (secretly, to use the bathroom) existed because of the Escarpment; that our house stood upon that cuesta. If I consider now what I want people to know about the Escarpment in New York, it would be far more than I knew when I lived there; it would be what I'm learning as I return from the far end of its arc.

* * *

An online article, "A Giant Beneath Us," claims the Niagara Escarpment is "far and away the most important and prominent geologic aspect of Western New York" though it "is mostly unknown" throughout the region. The Executive Director of the Western New York Land Conservancy wants it to become "a really well established and well-known community icon." To protect it from development, the group acquired the Niagara Escarpment Preserve, a 36.5-acre property northwest of Lockport, and works with the "Restore the Gorge" project along the Niagara River. However, once past the Falls and the Gorge, few places in New York refer to the Escarpment and few references to its length and location agree.

The Silurian Niagaran strata encircles the lower Great Lakes, but the southernmost half is largely underground. The image of the escarpment as an arc centers on the strata's visible surface exposure. In New York, along the southern side of the Ontario Plain, the escarpment reveals its structure in only a handful of places and further south is buried beneath sediments of later geologic periods.

In western New York we can understand how landscapes are shaped across time, dependent on changes in sea and lake levels, the extent of recurring glaciation, the flooding and draining of glacial meltwaters. As elsewhere, where Lakes Algonquin and Nipissing formed beaches and lake plains at different altitudes, so in New York a series of plains and elevations spread south from Glacial Lake Iroquois, Lake Ontario's precursor. The original shoreline of Glacial Lake Iroquois, the Iroquois (or Ontario) Plain, extended to the

Niagara Escarpment. Lockport sits both on and below the Niagara Escarpment. The area due south on the Niagara Cuesta is the Tonawanda Plain, formerly the bed of Glacial Lake Tonawanda, which spread from Buffalo on the west nearly to Rochester in the east. The southern edge of the Tonawanda Plain is, in Bradford Van Diver's terms, "the rather inconspicuous Onondaga scarp," and beyond it is the Erie plain, including the Lake Erie basin. Lake Tonawanda was filled by an outlet of Lake Erie and drained into Lake Ontario through several outlets. As the land rose, all those outlets closed except for the one at Lewiston, where Niagara Falls began its long recession up the Niagara Gorge.

Eventually human history settled on the landscape, including a host of Native American tribes—a Neutral village once stood where Lockport would rise—and after the War of 1812, a host of European-American settlers and developers filled the landscape with villages, towns, farms, and cities. The Niagara Frontier occupies four counties east of the Niagara River on the Lake Ontario and Tonawanda Plains: Niagara, Orleans, Erie, and Genesee. With the addition of Monroe County surrounding Rochester, they encompass the Niagara Escarpment and the Niagara Cuesta in western New York and complete the staff supporting the arc of the Escarpment.

24

Crossing from Ontario on the International Bridge, we usually descended north into Lewiston and then traveled east on NY 104, the Ridge Road, perched below the Escarpment and above the Ontario Plain, paralleling Lake Ontario. We'd head to my father and stepmother's home in Newfane, halfway between Lockport and the lake. Sometimes, inconveniently, I took a back road, perhaps the Lower Mountain Road or more often the Upper Mountain Road, close to the lip of the Escarpment. The Upper Mountain Road ended at the outskirts of Lockport and joined a highway that began in Niagara Falls, crossed the unheralded cuesta, and in the middle of Lockport, skirted the Erie Canal, its channel carved through the Niagara Escarpment. The canal was the reason there was a Lockport.

In college, near Rochester, whenever chums from down-state airily mentioned "The City" or "The Island," instead of naming New York or Long Island, I casually alluded to "The Lake," pretending they knew I meant Ontario—they didn't. I should have referred to "The Canal" but never did. It couldn't stack up against a metropolis; it conjured no immediate images as Manhattan did, even among people who lived in western New York.

I was born and grew up in Lockport, where my mother was born and grew up, where my father's family settled in the mid-1930s, where my mother and father met in high school and eventually married. Alert to coincidence and synchronicity—perhaps too much so—I've realized that my existence depends not simply on my parents finding one another *there* but also on there being a *there* where they might meet. Lockport existed because, for vessels to pass between the Hudson River to the east and much higher Lake Erie to the west, locks were constructed here for them to ascend the Niagara Escarpment. No escarpment, no locks; no locks, no Lockport; no Lockport, no me.

Joyce Carol Oates, who grew up around Lockport, described it as "a city of vertiginously steep hills built on the banks of the Erie Barge Canal—Lockport's predominant feature—which cuts through it in a deep swath and divides it approximately in two." It began below those locks in 1824, expanded up the escarpment, spread across the cuesta, and eventually spanned the canal with the Big Bridge, at one time the world's widest bridge. That was a time of boatmen and mule drivers, of towpaths to pull barges along the canal, of burgeoning villages and landlocked ports on a man-made waterway—Lockport, Gasport, Middleport, Brockport—opening up the heart of the state beyond its lakeshores and riverbanks. Life was vital along the canal in those early years.

When the canal economy declined, Lockport depended on its manufacturing base, particularly automobile parts, in factories built farther from the canal and closer to the railroads. As Oates once noted, "the well-to-do sector is generally south of the canal, sloping upward; Lowertown, steeply downhill, has always been working-class, semi-industrial, relatively undeveloped." Lowertown, where the nineteenth century city started, became the tenements of European immigrants; the business district on the escarpment developed into a twentieth century city; the wealthy and affluent and comfortable moved outwards, away from the center. In time the imposing brick high school on Main Street was torn down, replaced by a supermarket and parking lot, while a new high school sprawled across acreage on the southern outskirts of the city.

This was the city of my youth in the forties and fifties, bustling, prosperous, affluent. It could afford four competing five-and-tens, abundant small businesses, office buildings with tenants up to the third floor, three ice-cream parlors, three newsstands, two movie theaters, two large hotels, a Main Street intersection with three massive stone banks, jewelers and shoe stores and haberdasheries alternating randomly up and down the street. It was a land of plenty, ignoring the canal except for picture postcards of the locks and the Big Bridge in drugstores, newsstands, and five-and-dimes. In the developing city the canal, despite its historic importance, often seemed like an obstacle. On Main Street it was out of sight behind business buildings, barely noticeable.

My street intersected the canal as Cottage Street on the south side, where I lived, and Church Street on the north side, where the family churches were. On Sundays we would drive down Cottage, cross the Big Bridge, and drive out Church to St. Patrick's for the 9:15 service, the "Children's Mass," to hear Father Roy Chrissy speak in a voice resembling that of Buffalo Bob Smith, Howdy Doody's friend. Often, later in the day, we would walk with my father down to Main Street to get the Sunday paper and a comic book apiece at Kipp's newsstand and maybe stop in the Crystal for an ice cream sundae or a shake. Sometimes we crossed Main Street to gaze into the canal. The closest the canal came to the life of downtown was exactly at that corner, Main and

Cottage, where the buildings got shallower as it angled up behind them, until there was space only for a sidewalk leading out onto the Big Bridge. Standing there to look at the canal, we hoped some vessel would pass through the locks. Joyce Carol Oates found "walk[ing] along the canal's high banks" "gazing down at the foaming, black water below" to be "mesmerizing. Framed by dizzyingly steep, stark stone walls," she thought, "the canal has the look of a nightmare domesticated by frequent viewings, like German woodcuts in an edition of the Grimms' fairy tales." She must have felt that way when she viewed it as a child. I found our view spellbinding but never knew how to react to what I saw.

Each time I visit Lockport again, those Sunday memories revive, and more: the times I walked above or along the canal, crossed the footbridge on a railroad trestle with friends, spied on hobo camps on the canal bank below the bridge; the times we scared ourselves below the Big Bridge imagining alligators flushed down city toilets living there, full grown and hungry. As a writing teacher later, I asked students to draw a quick map of their hometowns, marking locations that mattered to them. I modeled the approach by sketching Lockport on the blackboard, starting at the intersection of the canal, the Big Bridge, and our street, then adding personal landmarks beyond it. While students worked, I stared at the map, images and scenes playing across my interior screen, more locations preparing to be included.

The canal divided the city. In memory I cross it easily, wander north all the way to Outwater Park, on the very edge of the scarp, with its view of the Ontario Plain, hoping to glimpse Lake Ontario; wander through Lowertown to reach Reid's hot dog stand; wander west across the Big Bridge to my favorite toy store and the bowling alley where I was briefly a pin boy; wander south up past Willow Park, which our house bordered, and into the woods beyond. Closing my eyes and screening my memories, I walk or bike past a great many buildings I still know by name.

And now I'm back in Lockport, hoping the canal will teach me what I still need to learn about the Niagara Escarpment.

* * *

Work on the Erie Canal began in 1817 to provide passage from Albany to Buffalo and link the Hudson River and the Port of New York with Lake Erie and other Great Lakes. The western terminus would be the upper Niagara River. The change in elevation across its 365 miles was 573 feet and, to maintain the downstream flow of Great Lakes water, inconsistent topography required the construction of eighty-three locks and eighteen aqueducts. When canal builders reached the Escarpment, they needed to overcome a sixty-foot change in elevation, and the channel would have to be carved through the Niagara Cuesta.

For centuries after the Wisconsin Ice Sheet receded, Lake Tonawanda flooded the cuesta south of the Escarpment. Drainage at multiple sites included two spillways at Lockport, channels of Eighteen Mile Creek spilling over the edge of what was termed the Mountain Ridge. Engineers decided on the eastern Lockport spillway as the route of the canal, giving them a leg up on excavation. For nineteenth century Americans, Carol Sheriff writes in *The Artificial River*, "the destruction of natural fixtures was as impressive as the construction of artificial ones." The "most impressive example of flattening mountains" she identifies as "the three-mile 'deep cut' at Lockport," "an artificial gorge" that "let boats pass thirty feet below the natural elevation at Lockport." Cadwallader Colden's 1825 *Memoir* included two illustrations of the Deep Cut, one showing the excavation in progress, the other displaying the result, a long straight channel of high walls dwarfing a canal boat with passengers standing on the roof. Travel writer Caroline Gilman wrote in 1838, "Here the great Erie Canal has defied nature, and used it like a toy ..." The Deep Cut exposed the strata of the Niagara Escarpment most nakedly, without the distraction of the double set of five lock flights and their accouterments. The Erie Canal and the Lockport Locks occasioned a celebration of the artistry of American engineers and builders; some enthu-

siasts claimed that the canal completed a design originated in nature or proudly fulfilled the intentions of God, who silently endorsed the westward expansion of American commerce.

Nearly a hundred years later, after railroads controlled transportation and commerce, the canal was widened and deepened, the southern locks reconstructed into two rather than five flights, and the northern locks closed. Today, the New York State Canal System consists of a network of canals serving both cargo and recreational traffic; townspeople and tourists still stand along bridges and canal banks watching vessels lock through.

The Erie Canal Heritage Trail, a biking and walking path established on the old northern towpath where mules and horses once trudged, starts near the Big Bridge, descends along the locks to the lower channel and ends in Lowertown. Visitors cross bridges above the five-flight channel to the center of the locks. Strolling down past the locks, they can look up from the point where westbound passengers first encountered them 200 years ago.

Many visual interpretations of what happened here were positioned on the east. Even the earliest drawings record buildings rising above the locks. Patrick McGreevy includes a portion of Raphael Beck's mural "Opening of the Erie Canal, October 26, 1825" on the cover of his book *Stairway to Empire: Lockport, the Erie Canal, and the Shaping of America*—the entire mural, installed in a Lockport bank for the canal's centennial, is now in the Niagara County Historical Society with a reproduction at the Erie Canal Discovery Center. McGreevy notes the mural's "sheer size and grandiose tone," its emphasis on "the nationalistic connotations of Lockport's moment: the flags at the top of the locks point west into the continent's interior," a "quintessentially progressive view." The locks rise monumentally up the background, a large canal boat crowded with rooftop passengers approaching below, a couple vessels already at their base. In the foreground, on a bluff, two men, a woman, and a child, all well dressed and apparently prosperous, stand near a soldier holding an American flag while behind them another soldier discharges a celebratory cannon. Other onlookers sit and stand around them. It's a stirring scene, even if the scale of it is somewhat exaggerated.

In the mural, the sheer escarpment walls on either side of the basin seem like nothing less than cliffs. At the actual locks, however, where the scale of the area is less imposing than Beck portrays it, there's little evidence of the escarpment. The walls on either side have been reinforced with stone and concrete and the natural scarp has been obscured. I wander between the locks, climbing well-worn flights of stairs, crossing narrow bridges and walkways on closed locks. A couple vessels enter, gates close behind them, waters raise them to the next level, other gates open, and the process repeats itself until the boats have sailed toward the deep cut. I have to go where they're going.

* * *

There are caves underneath Lockport. Someone tried to open one up for tourists. From what I now know about the formation of caves and sinkholes in the cuesta, I imagine the escarpment here has many hidden caves. One prominent and accessible cave is the site of the Lockport Caves Tour, its office above the canal, its entrance off the Heritage Trail.

On the noon tour, Ken, our guide, leads a dozen of us down the trail with intermittent pauses to fill us in about the history of Lockport, the locks, and the canal. He's knowledgeable and entertaining, explaining that scenes in *Sharknado 2* were filmed in the Lockport Cave. Past the Locks and remnant stone wall ruins Ken unlocks the entrance door to a large lighted metal tube and then ushers us into a well-constructed, dimly lighted room that will take us into the tunnel proper and the stone interior of the escarpment.

The New York State Legislature authorized construction of a tunnel on the north side of the canal in 1839, to provide waterpower for a mill. Eventually Birdsall Holly, an entrepreneur and hydraulic engineer, expanded the excavation into a 1,600-foot-long downward sloping tunnel for hydromechanical power. He constructed a seven-story factory and devised a water distribution system giving firefighters a more powerful fire-fighting option—ironically, one night a worker in the fire hydrants building knocked a lantern over and the factory burned down.

We pass through a stone arch doorway into a lower, narrower passage. The walls are rough and uneven and the lighting minimal. We walk carefully single file on a narrow gravel path along a continuous pool of water, pausing sometimes to consider the limestone walls. Water seeps through the rock and forms small stalactites and traces of flowstone. Irish laborers worked eight years to complete the tunnel in tight, dark, enclosed underground space.

At the far end of the cave the tunnel floor is flooded. We board a long flat boat lined with benches to float deeper into the escarpment, almost up to the top end of the cave but not as far as the water channel goes. In the dank semi-darkness, we sense the weight of the dolostone strata above us and in the uneven walls understand the challenge of chipping away all that subterranean stone by hand. Back at the dock, everyone is relieved to be shown a nearby exit—we won't retrace our footsteps to where we started.

Outside, in daylight, starting a steep climb to the escarpment's edge, it feels good to be out of the cave.

* * *

Before stopping at the headquarters of the Lockport Locks & Erie Canal Cruise in Lowertown, I drive past and cross the canal to Reid's Drive-In for an unnecessary but nostalgic red-with (hot dog with sauce)—only one, no fries—and a root beer rather than a milkshake, admitting I'm no longer the teenager who ate here almost nightly in summers. Then I drift back to the cruise site.

A dozen of us board the vessel, climb to the upper deck, and settle near the bow. The boat slips away into the canal's muddy water to slowly approach the open gates of the lower lock. We glide inside, its walls rising far above us. Steep staircases link the upper level of this lock with the top of the next gate. Discoloration on the walls signals how high we'll slowly be lifted once gates close and water pours below us. It takes twenty minutes to pass through the locks. The vessel floats at the upper line, the gates of the second lock open, and we motor in to repeat the process. Onlookers on the bridge near the gates watch our progress. Our view grows wider the higher we rise and then we're at the level of the upper canal, the Big Bridge gaping before us.

Passing through the city under the Big Bridge and the Triway Bridge and along stone buildings constructed from material excavated from the canal bed, we gain little sense of the escarpment. The business section of town keeps its back to the canal on either side. The escarpment forms the narrow foundation of the bridges and buildings, its depths hidden by the brown, murky waters. We will pass sections of canal banks that I explored with friends decades ago, but from the water I have little sense of where we are. Beyond the city, the banks are overgrown with trees and bushes, their limbs hanging out above the canal, some bending toward the channel, slender trunks occasionally hanging upside down into the water. The undergrowth is thick and inaccessible from the canal. Sometimes flora finds a foothold in joints and fractures, but more often the rock seems impenetrable.

Eventually the canal walls loom higher and we can appreciate the scale of the Deep Cut, so vaunted in Erie Canal history. In some places it's clear where strata were chopped away, evening out the layers; in other places the strata are more uneven and weathered. There seems to be no ready access to the canal from the escarpment or from the canal to the cliff top. We float only a short way into the Deep Cut, far enough to appreciate the effort it took to carve it by hand through the Escarpment.

Returning to the locks, we make a twenty-minute descent through them, then cruise through Lowertown to the Widewaters Marina near the intersection of Market Street and Cold Springs Road. Somewhere on that stretch we pass the house where my grandmother's oldest sister and her family lived. Cold Springs Road is familiar too; I'd been on it the day before, visiting family graves in the Cold Springs Cemetery and chatting amiably with the departed. As the boat turns around, I try to think about the eastward flow of the canal. It will stay below the Escarpment almost to Rochester and then rise onto the cuesta again.

I'll follow the Escarpment as far as I can. I've passed the place where my past intersects the Niagara Escarpment. I don't have that much farther to go.

25

It's easy to be unaware of the geologic history of the land you live on. The world Wordsworth thought was "too much with us"—where "getting and spending, we lay waste our powers"—is as much with us as ever. "Little we see in Nature that is ours," he lamented. I feel that less in well-wooded sites along the Escarpment, but drifting around the Niagara Frontier, my original home ground, I realize how superficial my past sense of it has been. The world was very much with me growing up. It takes effort, curiosity, and persistence to see into the topography beneath the places I knew then; only slowly do I appreciate how where I am now came to be here.

Having backtracked across the arc of the Escarpment to my starting point, I recognize my familiarity with the terrain, despite changes occurring on its surface over decades. Memories often emerge unbidden, but don't keep me from deepening my familiarity beyond my earlier knowledge. It's as if I've come to feel solidly rooted to the ground beneath the ground beneath my feet.

A part of me feels as if I've come as far as I need to come. And yet . . .

And yet, another part of me is unsettled by that thought. I haven't simply traveled on or along the Niagara Escarpment these thousand-some miles and uncounted days—I've traveled *with* the Niagara Escarpment, companionably aware of its personality, its moods, its mutability. Where I am now is only where *I* first intersected with its trajectory. We don't have that much farther to travel together, but I feel obliged to follow the arc of the Escarpment to *its* end.

* * *

The landscape Glacial Lake Tonawanda covered on the Niagara Cuesta is sometimes called the Huron Plain—in the glacial past an earlier, larger Lake Huron flowed across it—or the Tonawanda Plain—where an arm of the Niagara River arcs around Grand Island, Tonawanda Creek marks the line between Niagara and Erie counties. In the past I was barely aware of the Ontario Plain, the lowlands north of the Escarpment. Often at Outwater Park, on Lockport's northern edge, I would stop at its overlook hoping to glimpse distant Lake Ontario across the Ontario Plain, which we crossed to reach the beach town of Olcott or, later, Newfane, where my father and stepmother lived and are buried. The Tonawanda Plain, which we unknowingly crossed on any excursion south on Transit Road to Buffalo or Erie County, was simply a flat stretch of landscape, unheralded, unidentified.

But it has seeped more solidly into my consciousness while exploring the Niagara Gorge and the Lockport Locks. Glacial Lake Iroquois once surged against the Niagara Escarpment and Glacial Lake Tonawanda once spilled over the Escarpment through half a dozen spillways. Over time Lake Iroquois shrank into Lake Ontario and the Ontario Plain emerged; the slow rebound of the Tonawanda Plain in the recession of the Ice Sheet tilted the basin of Lake Tonawanda, shriveling each spillway until only the most western one provided drainage, the Niagara River.

Two branches of a single stream, Eighteen Mile Creek, created neighboring spillways at Lockport. The eastern branch served for construction of the Lockport Locks, and the Deep Cut through "the Mountain Ridge" followed that channel; the western branch was exploited for quarrying. Scholars and journalists sometimes compare the Lockport spillways to Niagara Falls because its two channels separated from one another just as the Niagara River did at Goat Island, and, thousands of years ago, the "Gulf" forming below the Escarpment started to replicate the Niagara Gorge. The spillways eroded at different rates and, by the time the land rebounded and Lake Tonawanda's waters flowed chiefly to the Lewiston spillway, they were simply creeks, their "gulf" considerably shrunken. Little at what is presently the Rollin T. Grant Gulf Wilderness Park invites that Niagara comparison now. The Gulf Wilderness ravine is not deep, and its slopes are well hidden under forest undergrowth and abundant trees. Indian Falls, its main scenic feature, is a low series of relatively flat steps that midsummer flow doesn't always inundate. Beyond the park the two Lockport spillways converge again, uniting in the Gulf and joining other tributaries of Eighteen Mile Creek to flow toward Lake Ontario.

As a boy I sometimes went with friends to skinny-dip at Indian Falls, circuiting through Outwater Park and Glenview Cemetery to get there. I never knew that the ravine we wandered in had any connection with the Locks or the Deep Cut or with Niagara Falls. Even as I walk the Gulf Wilderness trails now, I have trouble making those connections.

* * *

The transformation of the Glacial Lake Tonawanda spillways over thousands of years reduced them from broadly torrential to narrowly placid—at times, the waterways are barely wet. The development of the lands around them from wilderness to agriculture or industry or residences also reduced them in both power and presence, isolating them off rural byways. Each spillway is part of a creek that starts on the Niagara Cuesta and winds its way—sometimes with astonishing circuitry—to empty into Lake Ontario. At Gulf Wilderness the waterway joins the main branch of Eighteen Mile Creek flowing north and, just beyond Ridge Road, meets the East Branch of Eighteen Mile Creek flowing from Royalton Ravine, near Gasport, ten miles east. The enlarged Eighteen Mile Creek empties into the lake at Olcott. The Oak Orchard Creek at Medina Falls flows north from the wetlands of the Iroquois National Wildlife Refuge on the border of Orleans and Genesee Counties and, after passing under—(yes, under!)—the Erie Canal and plummeting into Glenwood Lake, continues to Oak Orchard State Marine Park. Holley Falls began as a falls on Sandy Creek, which carved out its glen and receded a mile south; a dam was installed to tap waterpower and only when the Barge Canal was constructed did Sandy Creek receive its overflow, carry it through the glen, and bring it to the lake east of Hamlin Beach State Park.

Intending to stop briefly at the remaining spillways, I head east out of Lockport on NY 31, Rochester Road. The names of the towns along the way are familiar —Gasport, Middleport, Medina, Albion, Holley, Brockport—reminding me of people I once knew at college, but I'm now more aware of the highlands often south of the highway, the lowlands to the north, the distant and invisible lake. I never before knew the route crossed the Ontario Plain. I occasionally turn south to climb a nearby hill and gain another sense of the Escarpment. Instead of returning to the highway when I leave Royalton Ravine Park near Gasport, I can't resist driving east on Mountain Road for a while, just to be riding along the Escarpment.

Medina Falls and Holley Falls are the most memorable of the existing spillways. A drone photographer, Joe Blake, posted videos of Medina Falls on YouTube, recording various levels of flow over a period of months. Most often the water stays centered on the creek bed but occasionally water levels rise to broaden and heighten the flow. On the July day I visit, the flow is intense enough to surge over the higher section of the scarp. I view it from above, walking the Erie Canal Heritage Trail on the north side of the canal, juxtaposing both geologic and industrial history.

Holley Falls is also close to the Erie Canal, on the outskirts of Holley, pleasantly secluded in Canal Park below surrounding escarpment slopes. I walk to either side of the falls, crossing the East Branch of Sandy Creek where it meets the waters from the falls or crossing on the roof of the tunnel that carries the creek out of the glen. The falls tumble down a series of steps and I have no luck determining how many steps there might be.

The presence of these spillways just off the familiar highway is cause for reflection. Until now they were unknown to me, but I can no longer think of the landscape without thinking of them. Having traced the Niagara Escarpment for roughly 1,100 miles to get back on familiar ground, I can't help feeling how unfamiliar it all is—in a sense, how unfamiliar it had always been—now that I can't help seeing it in terms of its underlying terrain.

Robert Root

* * *

A sign on the Pont des Rennes, the 858-foot-long pedestrian bridge spanning the gorge below High Falls in Rochester, claims that the Genesee River has its source in Potter County, Pennsylvania, and flows 155 miles across New York to discharge into Lake Ontario. The river once reached the lake through Irondequoit Bay, east of Rochester, but glacial debris closed that outlet, and the river made a new channel. From source to mouth the Genesee River makes a 1,984-foot change in elevation and creates several waterfalls along the way. Its gorge at Letchworth State Park, nearly 65 miles south of Lake Ontario, is celebrated as "the Grand Canyon of the East," its walls up to 600 feet high with three waterfalls plummeting over them. Passing through Rochester the Genesee flows over three more waterfalls.

As a student at State University College Geneseo, I was inspired by my Earth Science professor to visit the falls and gorge at Letchworth State Park. But it's only now, near the High Falls in Rochester, that I appreciate how handy the Genesee River would be for an earnest geology student. Tracing the river's descent from just below the Pennsylvania state line to the final level below Rochester's Lower Falls, that student could study strata between 350 million and 440 million years old. Depositions of the Devonian Period are evident in Letchworth State Park and Silurian depositions are found at High Falls, Middle Falls, and Lower Falls in Rochester. Like Niagara Falls, High Falls flows over Lockport Dolostone past Rochester Shale. The very names of those strata justify my being here.

I was on the Pont des Rennes a few years earlier, on the third day of a fiercely cold January, five days after Sue and I stood on a frigid and snowy Goat Island viewing the

American Falls. It is 110 feet high and extends along a long open gorge; High Falls is 96 feet high and the Genesee Gorge it empties into is rounded and ringed with buildings constructed to draw on its hydropower. The bridge across the Genesee that day provided a clear view of the falls, and the mist was thankfully slight. The river divided to pass around the island below the bridge and then headed placidly toward the lower two falls and the lake. Ice clung to portions of the gorge walls.

Now, in July, after recent thunderstorms, the Genesee runs high and the falls gush turbulent brown, the water thrusting out beyond the overhang and flooding the gorge. Most of the island is under water, and talus below gorge walls is partially submerged. The space below the overhang is hollowed out on either side of the falls. The Genesee has carved a great gorge here.

I wander slowly across the bridge, trying to see the falls and its gorge from every angle. The Rochester skyline rises around them.  The bridge offers the most unobstructed view and its distance from the falls fully exposes the strata of the gorge's eastern wall. The bushes above the wall seal its edge off from wanderers. Across the flooded plunge pool at the massive stone bridge near the edge of the falls, a train is passing; downstream the Genesee winds through tree-lined banks and under a busy highway bridge before curving past bare stone walls and out of sight.

On the east side of the gorge a short stretch of the incomplete Genesee Riverway Trail, intended to run from the Erie Canalway Trail to Lake Ontario past four parks designed by Frederick Law Olmstead, leads me to a higher point closer to the falls. It brings me nearer street traffic, but I hear only roaring waters. Remembering the woman who recorded the sound of Horseshoe Falls, I set my iPhone camera to video and hold it up to the river, capturing the wide, swirling current approaching the falls, their foaming, everchanging plunge over the edge, the rolling, shifting mist that rises from the pool. I record for only 30 seconds or so, but I stand watching and listening to High Falls for several minutes more, willingly entranced.

*   *   *

Standing on the Pont des Rennes, gazing at High Falls in one direction and the lower river bound for Lake Ontario in the other, I remind myself that the Genesee River had not been a spillway for Lake Tonawanda. That leads me to imagine what those spillways might have become had the land not risen, had their waterways continued to carve their plunge pools. If the bed of Lake Tonawanda hadn't shifted, the Niagara River would not have become the sole outlet of the Upper Great Lakes into Lake Ontario; they would have emptied into Lake Tonawanda, and it might have become the western terminus for the Erie Canal, thus eliminating the need for a deep cut through the Mountain Ridge and the construction of a double flight of locks there. No locks, no Lockport, I remind myself; no Lockport, no me. Once you start examining cause and effect, it seems ever more incomprehensible that you exist at all, especially if not only your ancestors but also the course of history and the forces shaping the earth itself had to align in the way they did in order for the result to be specifically you.

High Falls at the Genesee Gorge is not the end of the Niagara Escarpment, though it is the end of my travels in search of it. Geologists suggest various places beyond the Genesee River to which the Escarpment extends, mostly deep underground. The scope of Silurian strata that has underlain my travels is much broader than the arc of the Escarpment. The cuesta is not the escarpment. East of Rochester, the Niagara Escarpment, the Tonawanda Plain, where the Niagara Cuesta can be found, and the Onondaga Escarpment essentially merge. Somewhere further east there may well be an outcropping that would let me touch Niagaran earth again, as I did at Brady's Rocks in Wisconsin, but I won't search for it. I've come far enough and the sight of High Falls plummeting into the Genesee Gorge will suit me fine as the final image on the arc of the Escarpment.

On the next few nights, as I make my way back to Wisconsin, I play the video of High Falls several times, to get the sound of the falls more deeply into my consciousness, as a soundtrack for my memories of where I've been along the arc of the Escarpment.

Epilogue

An impulse to follow a path provided by nature can be irresistible. You step out onto a trail—or a shoreline or a formation—and wonder what it would be like to go where it begins or where it ends. But the destination isn't the goal; the goal is the journey itself.

And so I complete my traverse of the arc of the Escarpment. To retrace it I'll call on the memories and images I've accumulated. I'll stand on many of those sites again, especially those close to home, and just as my perspective on my childhood home ground altered on this trip, I'll have a different sense of them than I once did. Being at Brady's Rocks or High Cliff or anywhere on the Door Peninsula will connect me effortlessly to the arc of the escarpment across its full length.

In the past I've paid considerable attention to my origins, to ancestral links and family dynamics that influenced the way I operate in the world. Of late, my curiosity has centered on knowing *where* I am, and the arc of the Escarpment helped map my route to that discovery. I know something now about the land that has been my home ground throughout my life. By arousing that sense of place I located myself in a history of greater scope than ancestry can provide. At times, I feel positively Silurian, a particle of its sediment, and I have no illusions about the significance such a particle has in such a span of history.

A map of the Niagara Escarpment often shows up online, with a red line arcing from New York through Ontario and Michigan into Wisconsin. How little that image tells me about what it means to be grounded at any point along that trajectory. I've filed hundreds of photographs in laptop folders, images that help me remember locations and formations: bluffs and cliffs, cataracts and gorges, crevices and caves, sea stacks and alvars, islands and peninsulas, sinkholes and springs, shorelines and quarries. If I close my eyes after viewing one of them, I can feel myself standing on a prospect, listening to waves and waterfalls and woodland winds or to the silence within the cuesta. So much of it stays with me, comes back to me at the slightest provocation, and because the arc of the Escarpment encompasses most of the major milestones of my life, personal memories surface as well: childhood, youth, adulthood, and beyond. My experience with the arc of the escarpment has surprisingly given me a spiritual certainty about existence.

If I am but a particle of Silurian strata, that strata has endured for an almost inconceivable length of time and will endure for an almost unimaginable time to come. But the escarpment reminds me by its crumbling from the face of its cuesta that mutability is part of its nature too, that the very rocks we stand upon are impermanent. I wrote this while news reports kept me current with volcanic eruptions in south Pacific islands, edited it while southern states were flooding, and Asian countries felt earthquakes and tsunamis. The earth reminds us often that it is not dormant. Connecting to the land we temporarily occupy at least links us to the vast ages of planetary existence, links us by proxy to all living things that ever were and ever will be, including the very earth itself. It's not immortality but it's an existence long enough for me.

I take comfort in knowing not simply *who* I am but *where* I am. I expect it to endure a while, this contentment I find by locating myself in the arc of the Escarpment.

Acknowledgments

Thanks to those who spurred my interest in the Niagara Escarpment and aided the growth of my understanding: Eric Fowle of the Niagara Escarpment Resource Network, Sherrill Anderson of the Lakeshore Natural Resource Partnership, Jim Urinak, William Mode, John Lucazj, Joanne Kluessendorf, Bob Bultman, Dan Collins and Nancy Aten, David Mickelson, Daryl Cowell, David Webster, Mark Zelinski, Roger Kuhns, Marlin Johnson, and Will Stewart.

The book has benefited from the efforts of the editorial and production staffs at Cornerstone Press, including publisher Dr. Ross Tangedal, editors Brett Hill, Grace Dahl, and Ellie Atkinson, and Ava Willet, Sophie McPherson, and Natalie Reiter on the media and sales staff.

Some much-altered portions of this book were published as:

"Caves," *Kentucky English Bulletin*, 65:2 (2016), 64-68.

"Crossing the Cuesta," *Elemental: A Collection of Michigan Creative Nonfiction*, ed. Anne-Marie Oomen. Detroit: Wayne State University Press, 2018: 138-146

"Hiking Wisconsin with 'Ghosts' of the Ice Age," *Zocalo Public Square*, http://www.zocalopublicsquare.org/2017/12/01/hiking-wisconsin-ghosts-ice-age/ideas/essay/

"Seul Choix Point, Michigan: Of Shells and Strata, Time and Terrain," *The Great Lakes Review*, January 29, 2017, http://greatlakesreview.org/seul-choix-point-michigan-of-shells-and-strata-time-and-terrain/

"Time and Terrain," *Split Rock Review*, Issue 10: (2018) https://www.splitrockreview.org/root

I'm grateful to those editors and publishers.

I'm also thankful for those in my family who supported my research, tolerated my absences, and sometimes shared my ramblings, all of which made the book possible.

Select Bibliography

Birmingham, Robert A., and Leslie E. Eisenberg. *Indian Mounds of Wisconsin*. Madison: University of Wisconsin Press, 2000.

Blei, Norbert. *Door Steps: The Days, The Seasons*. Peoria: Ellis Press, 1983.

Blocksma, Mary. *The Fourth Coast: Exploring the Great Lakes Shoreline from the St. Lawrence Seaway to the Boundary Waters of Minnesota*. New York: Penguin, 1995.

Colden, Cadwallader D. *Memoir, Prepared at the Request of a Committee of the Common Council of the City of New York, and Presented to the Mayor of the City, at the Celebration of the Completion of the New York Canals*. New York: Printed by the Order of the Corporation of New York, by W. A. Davis, 1825.

Coniglio, Mario, Paul Karrow, and Peter Russell. *Manitoulin Rocks! Rocks, Fossils, and Landforms of Manitoulin Island*. Waterloo, CA: Earth Science Museum, University of Waterloo, 2007.

Curl, Rane L. "The Fiborn Limestone: Geological History, Quarry Area Features, and its Place in 19th Century Sault Ste. Marie Industry," in Whitney, Mark. *Fiborn Quarry, Then and Now*. Ann Arbor: Michigan Karst Conservancy, 2014.

Dorr, John A., Jr., and Donald F. Eschman. *Geology of Michigan.* Ann Arbor: University of Michigan Press, 1977.

Dott, Robert H., Jr., and John W. Attig. *Roadside Geology of Wisconsin.* Missoula: Mountain Press Publishing Company, 2004.

Ehlers, George M. *Stratigraphy of the Niagaran series of the Northern Peninsula of Michigan.* Museum of Paleontology: Papers on Paleontology No. 3. Ann Arbor: University of Michigan Museum of Paleontology, 1973.

"A Giant Beneath Us: The Niagara Escarpment," http://www.wgrz.com/news/article/200180/10/A-Giant-Beneath-Us-The-Niagara-Escarpment, February 10, 2013.

Green, Doris. *Wisconsin Underground: A Guide to Caves, Mines, And Tunnels in and around the Badger State.* Black Earth, WI: Trails Books, 2000.

Hunt, Mary Hoffman, and Don Hunt. *Hunt's Guide to Michigan's Upper Peninsula.* Albion, MI: Midwestern Guides, 2001.

Important Bird Areas of Wisconsin: Critical Sites for the Conservation and Management of Wisconsin Birds. Ed. Yoyi Steele. Madison: Wisconsin Department of Natural Resources, 2007.

Kelly, Peter E., and Douglass W. Larson. *The Last Stand: A Journey Through the Ancient Cliff-Face Forest of the Niagara Escarpment.* Toronto: Natural Heritage Books, 2007.

Klussendorf, Joanne, and Donald G. Mikulic. "Bedrock Geology of the Door Peninsula of Wisconsin," *Wisconsin's Door Peninsula: A Natural History.* Ed. John C. Palmquist. Appleton: Perin Press, [ca. 1989].

Koysdar, Richard. *Natural Landscapes of the Niagara Escarpment*. Dundas: Tierceron Press, 1996.

Lapham, Increase. Letter to His Wife, quoted in Klussendorf, Joanne, and Donald G. Mikulic. "Bedrock Geology of the Door Peninsula of Wisconsin," *Wisconsin's Door Peninsula: A Natural History*. Ed. John C. Palmquist. Appleton: Perin Press, [ca. 1989].

Lapham, I. A. *The Antiquities of Wisconsin, as Surveyed and Described*. Washington: Smithsonian Institution, 1855; repr. Madison: University of Wisconsin Press, 2001.

Link, Mardi Jo. *The Drummond Girls: A Story of Fierce Friendship Beyond Time and Chance*. New York: Grand Central Publishing, 2015.

Linnabery, Ann Marie. "The Niagara Discoveries: The Lockport Gulf," *Lockport Union-Sun and Journal*, February 18, 2017.

Luczaj, John A. "Geology of the Niagara Escarpment in Wisconsin," *Geoscience Wisconsin* 22:1 (2013): 1-34. wgnhs.org/pdfs/geoscipdf/GS22-a01.pdf

Manthorne, Katherine E. "Hudson River: Global Thoroughfare," *American Arts Quarterly* 26:4 (Fall 2009). http://www.nccsc.net/essays/hudson-river

McGreevy, Patrick. *Stairway to Empire: Lockport, the Erie Canal, and the Shaping of America*. Albany: State University of New York Press, 2009.

McLean, Ross, Anne Cruik, and John Shenk. *Country Walks: The Niagara Escarpment*. Toronto: Stoddard, 1994.

Mickelson, David M., Louis J. Maher Jr., and Susan L. Simpson. *Geology of the Ice Age National Scenic Trail.* Madison: University of Wisconsin Press, 2011.

Minot, Lydia David. "Sketches of Scenery on Niagara River," *The North American Review* 2:6 (March 1816).

Muir, John. *The Life and Letters of John Muir.* V. 1. Ed. William Frederic Badé. Boston: Houghton-Mifflin, 1923.

Niagara Escarpment Resource Network. "Wisconsin's Niagara Escarpment: Physiographic/Cultural Sub-Unit Divides." NEPhysiographicMap_032909.pdf. 2006.

Oates, Joyce Carol. "American Gothic," *The New Yorker* (May 8, 1995).

Oomen, Anne-Marie. "Finding (My) America. IV. The Alvar," *An American Map.* Detroit: Wayne State University Press, 2010.

Pearen, Shelley J. *Exploring Manitoulin.* 3rd Ed. Toronto: University of Toronto Press, 2001.

Powers, Tom. *Michigan State and National Parks: A Complete Guide.* Fourth Edition. Holt, MI: Thunder Bay Press, 2007.

rotorhead85. "The Washington Island Expedition," http://www.travbuddy.com/travel-blogs/41179/summary

Sheriff, Carol. *The Artificial River: The Erie Canal and The Paradox of Progress, 1817-1862.* New York: Hill & Wang, 1996.

Shrock, Robert R. "Geology of Washington Island and Its Neighbors, Door County, Wisconsin," *Transactions of the Wisconsin Academy of Sciences, Arts and Letters,* Vol. 32 (1940): 199-227.

Stephens, Lorina, and Gary Stephens. *Touring the Giant's Rib: A Guide to the Niagara Escarpment.* Toronto: Stoddart Publishing, 1993.

Strand, Ginger. *Inventing Niagara: Beauty, Power, and Lies.* New York: Simon & Schuster, 2008.

Taylor, Keith. "Drummond Island Fossils," *Fidelities: A Chronology.* Ann Arbor: Alice Greene & Co., 2015.

Tesmer, Irving H., Ed. *Colossal Cataract: The Geological History of Niagara Falls.* Albany: State University of New York Press, 1981.

The History of Waukesha County Wisconsin. Chicago: Western Historical Society, 1880; Rev. Ed. Waukesha County Historical Society, 1976.

Thwaites, Reuben Gold. *Down Historic Waterways: Six Hundred Miles of Canoeing Upon Illinois and Wisconsin Rivers.* 3rd Ed. Chicago: A. C. McClurg, 1910.

Tovell, Walter M. *Guide to the Geology of the Niagara Escarpment: With Field Trips.* Ed. Lorraine Brown. Ontario: Niagara Escarpment Commission/Ontario Heritage Commission, 1992.

Van Diver, Bradford B. *Roadside Geology of New York.* Missoula: Mountain Press Publishing, 1985.

Van Diver, Bradford B. *Upstate New York, Field Guide.* Dubuque: Kendall/Hunt, 1980.

Wisconsin, naturally: A Guide to 150 Great State Natural Areas. Ed. Thomas Meyer. Madison: Wisconsin Department of Natural Resources, 2003.

ROBERT ROOT's narratives of history and place include *Recovering Ruth: A Biographer's Tale, Following Isabella: Travels in Colorado Then and Now,* and *Walking Home Ground: In the Footsteps of Muir, Leopold, and Derleth,* and the essay collection *Postscripts: Retrospections on Time and Place.* He is the editor of the anthology *Landscapes With Figures: The Nonfiction of Place* and co-editor of the anthology *The Fourth Genre: Contemporary Writers of/on Creative Nonfiction.* He has published and presented widely on creative nonfiction.

His essay "A Double Life," published in *Writing on the Edge,* won the 2007 Donald Murray Award for Best Essay on Writing and/or Teaching. "Postscript to a Postscript to 'The Ring of Time'," published in *The Pinch,* was nominated for a Pushcart Prize and won the Council of Wisconsin Writers Short Nonfiction Award. He has been an Artist-in-Residence at Acadia National Park, Rocky Mountain National Park, and Isle Royale National Park, and a visiting writer at the Kachemak Bay, Sanibel Island, and Geneva Writers Conferences. He lives in Waukesha, Wisconsin.

Further information is available at www.rootwriting.com.

Printed in the USA
CPSIA information can be obtained
at www.ICGtesting.com
CBHW030154221223
2847CB00003B/74